Songs of

THE BRITISH MUSIC HALL

Compiled and edited
with a critical
history of the songs
and their times

by
Peter Davison

Music Editor: Jerry Silverman
Musical Autographer: Donald Ashwander
Book Designer: Jean Hammons

Copyright © 1971 by Oak Publications,
A Division of Embassy Music Corporation, New York, NY.

International Standard Book Number: 0.8256.0099.5
Library of Congress Catalog Card Number: 69-13423

Exclusive Distributors:
Music Sales Corporation
24 East 22nd Street, New York, NY 10010 USA
Music Sales Limited
8/9 Frith Street, London W1V 5TZ England
Music Sales Pty. Limited
120 Rothschild Street, Rosebery, Sydney, NSW 2018, Australia

Printed in the United States of America by
Vicks Lithograph and Printing Corporation

TO SHEILA

London is a large village on the Thames where
the principal industries carried on are music
halls and the confidence trick.

Dan Leno

Every art contributes to the greatest art of
all, the art of living.

Bertolt Brecht

A dirty mind is a perpetual feast.

Ally Sloper

Index of Song Titles

6   *Acknowledgements*

8   *Foreword*

204   A Little Bit Of Cucumber
     — *Harry Champion*

26   A Motto For Every Man — *Harry Clifton*

152   A Thing He Had Never Done Before
     — *George Robey*

84   And Her Golden Hair Was Hanging
     Down Her Back — *Alice Leamar*
     and Sir Seymour Hicks

80   Are We To Part Like This Bill?
     — *Kate Carney*

198   'Arf A Pint Of Ale — *Gus Elen*

63   At My Time Of Life — *Herbert Campbell*

157   Bang Went The Chance Of A Lifetime
     — *George Robey*

16   Champagne Charlie — *George Leybourne*

30   Cushie Butterfield

50   Don't Go Out To-night, Dear Father

102   Every Little Movement — *Marie Lloyd*

136   Following In Father's Footsteps
     — *Vesta Tilley*

220   Half-Past Nine or My Wedding Day
     — *Nellie Wallace*

201   Have You Paid The Rent?
     — *Harry Champion*

224   Heaven Will Protect An Honest Girl
     — *Gracie Fields*

38   He's Going to Marry Mary Ann
     — *Bessie Bellwood*

88   His Lordship Winked At The Counsel
     — *Harry Rickards*

128   I Live In Trafalgar Square — *Morny Cash*

192   If It Wasn't For The 'Ouses In Between
     — *Gus Elen*

144   It's Alright In The Summertime
     — *Vesta Victoria*

77   I've Got Rings On My Fingers
     — *Ellaline Terriss*

106   I've Never Lost My Last Train Yet
     — *Marie Lloyd*

188   "Jeerusalem's" Dead!
     — *Albert Chevalier*

46   Keep Your Feet Still, Geordie Hinney

92 Lily Of Laguna — *Eugene Stratton*

118 My Fiddle Is My Sweetheart
     — *G. H. Chirgwin*

120 My Fiddle Was My Sweetheart
     — *G. H. Chirgwin*

174 Nanny — *Harry Lauder*

110 One Of The Deathless Army
     — *Little Tich*

132 Penny Whistler — *Paul Mill*

148 Prehistoric Man — *George Robey*

13 Sam Hall — *W. G. Ross*

177 Seaweed — *Fred Earle*

168 That's The Reason Noo I Wear A Kilt
     — *Harry Lauder*

114 The Fire Was Burning Hot
     — *T. E. Dunville*

182 The Future Mrs. 'Awkins
     — *Albert Chevalier*

56 The Huntsman — *Dan Leno*

212 The Man Was A Stranger To Me
     — *George Formby Sr.*

162 The Music-Hall Shakespeare
     — *Emil Clare*

68 The Swimming Master — *Dan Leno*

20 Villikins And His Dinah
     — *Frederick Robson*

140 Waiting At The Church — *Vesta Victoria*

208 We All Go To Work But Father
     — *J. C. Heffron*

216 We All Went Home In A Cab
     — *George Formby, Sr.*

98 When I Take My Morning Promenade
     — *Marie Lloyd*

41 Wor Nanny's A Mazer

34 Wotcher 'Ria — *Bessie Bellwood and
     Nelly Farren*

74 Young Men Taken In And Done For
     — *Dan Leno*

124 You've Got A Long Way To Go
     — *Frank Coyne*

229 *Afterword*

238 *Bibliography*

240 *Recordings*

241 *General Index*

Acknowledgements

Many people have helped me directly or indirectly in the preparation of this book, from those who have dug out old records from their attics to the editorial staff of Oak Publications, whose encouragement and advice have been greatly appreciated. As the book is largely dependent upon printed music and old recordings it is appropriate that I should first acknowledge my debt to the music publishers who own the copyrights of most of the songs given here.

Considerable care has been taken to ensure that all copyrights are accurately and faithfully acknowledged but, as anyone who has had experience of tracing the copyright of music-hall material will know, this is often a difficult task. Early recordings often attribute songs and acts to those who did not write them; copyright labels are often missing; and on occasion the wrong copyright labels are attached to records made half-a-century ago. Although specific acknowledgement of copyright is made individually for each song, I should, in addition, like to record my appreciation of the help given me by music publishers and also the Performing Right Society. In particular I should like to thank Mr. Bernard L. Brown, Manager of Campbell Connelly & Co. Ltd.; Mr. D. Elmes, Copyright Manager of Herman Darewski Music Publishing Co., and B. Feldman & Co. Ltd.; and Mr. F. Blackburn and Mr. K. Chipperfield of the Copyright Department of Francis, Day & Hunter, Ltd., for going to such lengths to seek out details of copyright, even of songs which they were aware from the first were not theirs. In this respect I should also like to thank Mr. Frederick Woods of the Performing Right Society Ltd., and Mr. Peter Gammond (who also provided me with the words of an earlier version of "Half-Past Nine"). I am also indebted to Lawrence & Wishart for permission to publish quotations from Robert Tressel's *The Ragged Trousered Philanthropists.*

This book relies only slightly on personal experience of music halls for, though I went to a music hall for the first time twenty-five years ago, they were past their prime then and at that time my interest was not deeply aroused by what they had to offer. My serious interest in music hall began about six years ago when I was examining the relationship between contemporary drama and popular dramatic forms such as monologues and cross-talk acts. I was helped initially by the Record Library of the Australian Broadcasting Commission in Sydney where I was allowed to listen to a large number of records made in the thirties and forties: I owe the A.B.C. special thanks for helping me at a crucial moment in my study.

But the greatest debt I owe in this respect is to Mr. Roy Jones of Birmingham, a private collector of early operatic recordings. When I returned to England from Australia I decided to try to build a collection of music-hall recordings and although I have gathered these from many places, it is to Roy Jones that I am indebted, not only for the bulk of my collection, but also for all kinds of information and advice about early recordings. I should also like to thank another enthusiast of early operatic recordings, John Boult, for playing various kinds of recordings—hill-and-dale, inner start, short- and long-play cylinders—on his equipment, and also for providing me with records.

I am grateful to David Greer for helping me to take down details of a number of songs from early recordings—often in a very poor condition making listening painful as well as difficult. Needless to say, he is not responsible for the music.

Just prior to writing this book in the summer of 1965, I was invited to discuss music-hall songs and acts in general, and one or two songs in detail, at two seminars run by the Centre for Contemporary Cultural Studies in the University of Birmingham. I am very grateful to the Centre, and particularly to Richard Hoggart and Stuart Hall, for the encouragement and criticism they gave me. Whether what I have now written will appeal to them I cannot tell; but, in comparing my first drafts with what I have now completed, I am aware of the extent to which they have helped free me from certain fixed literary critical inhibitions in discussing these songs. If I have failed, that is not, of course, to be laid at their door.

And now two personal acknowledgements. First to Mrs. Helen Tresahar in whose house I spent many years and from whom I learned something of the flavour of the theatrical life of Late Victorian and Edwardian England. I have also to thank her for books and illustrations—one or two of which, dedicated to her, appear in this volume, for she acted with Sir Seymour Hicks and Ellaline Terriss at the beginning of the century.

Lastly, an acknowledgment to my wife. She is accustomed to living virtually a separate life evening after evening, but at least I am usually devoting my time to some quiet pursuit—marking scripts or perhaps editing. But this book not only entailed the house being strewn with piles of fragile and precious records, and filled with a great deal of noise, often raucous and usually scratchy, but also her being asked to listen to snatches of recordings, played over and over again, to decide just what it was that those *so* articulate stars of the past actually said or sang.

Foreword

Music hall may evoke affectionate reminiscence or violent antipathy. For some it epitomises "the good old days"; for others it is the most degenerate of art forms. To some its artists had a vitality now lost and *their* songs had melodies that linger on; to others music hall was a compound of jingoistic sentimentality and vulgarity—perspiration rather than inspiration. Those were the days. . .

I exaggerate: but not much.

This book is not just a collection of songs, nor is it a history; still less is it composed of affectionate reminiscence. All the songs have points of interest and most are still enjoyable, but they do not make up a statistically exact sample of songs sung in the halls. Indeed, patriotic ballads are entirely absent (except as a point of reference). I have tried to assess what the songs chosen mean *now*, and how good they seem out of their original setting, rather than what glory they might once have had. I have also tried to show the significance of this tradition in the development of drama as a whole.

It is difficult, if not impossible, to talk about a poem or novel in such a way that the critical approach is acceptable to everyone. But at least there are a variety of ways in which a literary work of art can be discussed to the satisfaction of some coterie, however small. Drama presents for many critics even greater stumbling blocks than do poetry and the novel, and much drama suffers particularly from incomplete critical consideration. The fault lies not in the drama as such (bastard art though it may be) but in the language of criticism; and where a language is inadequate, so is comment. For popular drama there is little good, informed criticism in England (though *The Popular Arts* by Stuart Hall and Paddy Whannel is a recent honourable exception). For music hall, in particular, though there is plenty of reminiscence, a fair amount of history (often inaccurate), and some social study (at times, as in Christopher Pulling's, *They Were Singing*, very good indeed), detailed criticism scarcely exists. It is this gap that, with diffidence, I attempt, if not to fill, at least to enter.

Men have sung in groups gay and sad time out of mind. In the early nineteenth century many informal groups met in public houses and supper rooms; and, naturally enough, though anyone present might sing (as did the Colonel himself in the opening chapter of Thackeray's *The Newcomes*), some singers were more able than others. Singing for a supper, at least a liquid one, was a practicable possibility, as Thackeray indicates:

> Going to the play then, and to the pit, as was the
> fashion in those merry days, with some young fellows
> of my own age, having listened delighted to the most
> cheerful and brilliant of operas, and laughed enthusi-
> astically at the farce, we became naturally hungry at
> twelve o'clock at night, and a desire for welsh-rabbits
> and good old glee-singing led us to the "Cave of Harmony",
> then kept by the celebrated Hoskins, among whose
> friends we were proud to count.

> We enjoyed such intimacy with Mr. Hoskins that he
> never failed to greet us with a kind nod; and John the
> waiter made room for us near the President of the
> convivial meeting. We knew the three admirable glee-
> singers, and many a time they partook of brandy-and-
> water at our expense.
>
> *The Newcomes, Chapter 1*

The publican with a good eye to business was prepared to pay the able performer to attract him to his house.

Up and down the country, and especially in London, there were public houses and tavern gardens, supper rooms and cellars, where free entertainment was provided with the food and drink which were offered for sale. In 1854 one publican, Charles Morton, opened what is generally considered to be the first music hall: the New Canterbury. Food, drink, and entertainment still went together, but the small charge made at the entrance was specifically for the entertainment provided and this formalized the shift from saloon and supper-room entertainment to the music hall proper.[1]

The early halls always had a president or chairman who organized the proceedings; almost from the beginning, women appeared on stage and at least on certain

---

[1]Christopher Pulling gives an excellent short account of the development and decline of the music hall in the last four chapters of *They Were Singing*.

nights in the audience. In time, the relationship with the public house became looser and the likeness, particularly architecturally, to the legitimate theater became closer. By the 1870s the halls were enormously popular. Their days of glory lasted until a little before the first World War, but they lingered on between the Wars and quite recently have experienced a somewhat antiquarian revival.

Songs were always the mainstay of the halls but, as time went by, more and more patter was introduced into them, until wholly spoken acts became common. Gradually programmes became more varied in their content: jugglers, acrobats, wire-walkers, dancers, animals, and thought transference all appeared on the bills. Variety had taken the place of halls of music.

I have begun this collection of songs with a half-dozen that preceded the halls, or were sung in their early days; but only these, and those by George Formby Jr., Nellie Wallace, and Gracie Fields, are arranged roughly in period. The notes are critical, not historical or anecdotal, but I am deeply indebted to the work of others in these last respects, particularly to F. Chance Newton, W. Macqueen-Pope, M. Willson Disher, J. B. Booth, and Christopher Pulling. Formal acknowledgements to these gentlemen and to the music publishing companies who have been extremely kind and helpful are made in the appropriate places.

After the songs I have added a short Afterword. In this I have drawn some tentative conclusions from the commentary regarding the nature of these songs and their significance and have discussed briefly some of the critical difficulties and implications that have arisen.

The songs are given in forms 'conveniently available' though I have very often taken into account alternate versions, including recordings made as early as 1900, in preparing the versions given here. The problem of critical texts of popular songs such as these is a difficult one and I do not attempt to deal with it here. Occasionally I have given examples of alternatives where these may be of interest. Some songs have been reconstructed from recordings and for three of these only the choruses are given.

In the commentaries to the songs and in the Afterword I have drawn attention to what seem to me the virtues and weaknesses of music-hall songs, chiefly by specific reference to particular songs. In doing this I have consciously overstepped what are nowadays still usually accepted as the limits imposed upon critics: I have found it necessary to go beyond what appears on the printed page. This seems essential to me in dramatic criticism generally and in discussions of music hall in particular.

Although I have not set out to write a history as such, nor have I intended this book to be a collection of other people's reminiscences, the songs themselves, and the comments they elicit, are in themselves a history and biography of a kind —though the biography is that of the performers rather than of the authors and composers. Curiously, but surely appropriately, it is the nature and qualities of the stars who sang the songs, rather than those who wrote them, which may be perceived through the cold pages of print—as, for example, in "Wotcher 'Ria." That this should be so is one measure of the difference between music hall and more literary forms.

Imprecise and loose though the language of the music hall song so often is, yet paradoxically it reveals a fascination for language as language. Neither this delight in the use of words, nor the wonder of theatrical illusion which the music hall also revealed, could be claimed for the legitimate theater of this period. In addition to trying to draw attention to these characteristics, I have thought it worth discussing some of the implications that music hall has for contemporary drama. I have suggested, for example, why it is that the alienation of Brecht is likely to have very different effects in the English theater than in Germany, owing to the existence of certain characteristics of the English popular tradition. (Whether these implications will be disturbed by the constant breaking that occurs in commercial television drama through advertising remains to be seen.) I have also hinted at the debt which the 'absurd'—as it is understood in Britain— owes to popular drama.

The besetting sin of those who write on comedy and the comic is over-solemnity. I have tried not to be portentous in writing about these songs but, if one believes, as I do, that this subject, for all its gaiety and despite frequent crassness and triviality, ought to be considered seriously, then it is possible to sound too solemn or to seem to be seeking a profundity that does not exist. But, if the comment is not always apt, the songs are here to be enjoyed and discussed—and it is they that really matter.

Peter Davison
Birmingham, England: May, 1971

Sam Hall

Sung by W. G. Ross. Author and Composer Unknown.
Version Copyright: 1925, Chapman and Hall.

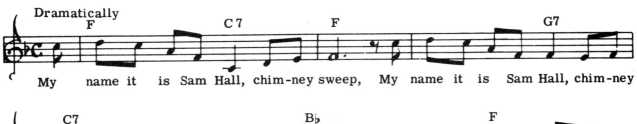

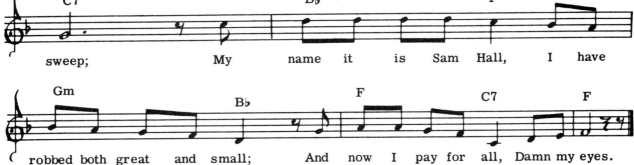

My name it is Sam Hall, Chimney Sweep,
My name it is Sam Hall, Chimney Sweep;
My name it is Sam Hall,
I have robbed both great and small,
And now I pay for all, Damn my eyes.

I killed a man they said, so they said,
I killed a man they said, so they said;
I dashed him on the head
With a great big lump of lead,
And left him there for dead, Blast his eyes.

They put me in the quod, in the quod,
They put me in the quod, in the quod;
They put me in the quod
And they tied me to a log,
And they left me there, by God,
  Damn their eyes.

Oh the preacher, 'e did come, 'e did come.
Yes, the preacher, 'e did come, 'e did come.
Oh the preacher 'e did come
And 'e talked of kingdom come.
He can kiss me bloody bum, Blast his eyes.

Oh the Sheriff, 'e came too, 'e came too;
Oh the Sheriff, 'e came too, 'e came too;
Oh the Sheriff, 'e came too,
With his boys all dressed in blue.
There'll be bloody work to do,
  Damn their eyes.

I goes up Holborn Hill in a cart,
I goes up Holborn Hill in a cart;
I goes up Holborn Hill,
At St. Giles I takes me gill,
And at Tyburn makes me will, Damn my eyes.

Then the Hangman, 'e comes too, 'e comes too;
Then the Hangman, 'e comes too, 'e comes too;
Then the Hangman, 'e comes too
With all his bloody crew
And he'll tell me what to do, Blast his eyes.

So it's up the rope I go, up I go,
So it's up the rope I go, up I go;
So it's up the rope I go
And I hear you bastards down below
Saying, "Sam, we told yer so!"
  Blast yer eyes.

I sees Molly in the crowd, in the crowd,
I sees Molly in the crowd, in the crowd;
I sees Molly in the crowd,
So I hollers right out loud,
"Molly, ain't yer bloody proud?" Damn yer eyes.

So this shall be my knell, be my knell;
So this shall be my knell, be my knell;
This is my funeral knell,
So I'll see you all in hell
And I hopes yer frizzle well,
  Blast yer eyes.

Strictly speaking, "Sam Hall" does not belong to the music hall, for it was sung—performed would be a better description—in one of the most disreputable forerunners of Morton's Canterbury: the Cyder Cellars in Maiden Lane, London. It has been suggested that Thackeray drew on the Cyder Cellars and the more respectable Evans's Supper Rooms for the Back Kitchen of *Pendennis* and the Cave of Harmony of *The Newcomes*. Clearly, from the opening chapter of the latter, what Captain Costigan could sing in the Back Kitchen (along with "The Body Snatcher" and "The Banner of Blood") did not please everyone at the Cave of Harmony and Thackeray intervenes to give this advice to "landlords" in the first number of *The Newcomes*, just a year before Morton opened the first music hall:

> If there are any "Caves of Harmony" now, I warrant Messieurs
> the landlords, their interests would be better consulted by keep-
> ing their singers within bounds.

It was just this that Charles Morton attempted to do, for glee-singing, opera, and even oratorio were not felt to be out of place in his hall of music.

"Sam Hall," with "Villikins and his Dinah," will serve as a reminder that the Canterbury gave but formal shape to a kind of entertainment that had been popular in eating and drinking places for many, many years. Ironically, both songs have survived the halls.

"Sam Hall" was exceptional in its own day and cannot be regarded as typical. It grew out of a tradition of street ballads about condemned men, and of a chimney sweep, Jack All, in particular. It has been traced back to a much older ballad about the pirate, Captain Kidd:

> My name was Captain Kidd,
> And God's laws I did forbid,
> And most wickedly I did,
> When I sailed.[1]

There is no single reliable version of "Sam Hall" and that printed here is constructed from several sources. In the broadside, Sam was ironically convicted for selling candles short of weight (though he also admits to theft). He is referred to as a chimney sweep in this ballad and also in some sung versions, so I have taken a verse to begin the song that tells first of his occupation and lesser crime. From then on, I have endeavoured to give a full version in something like logical progression. The fifth and seventh verses are repetitive and, in singing, the former could be omitted. The refrain often appears with a dash in "polite" versions, but in others, "Blast" and "Damn" are used exclusively or alternately, and there is a wide variation in who is damned or blasted. I have retained "my" in the first and sixth refrains, not because I regard Sam as admitting his guilt, but because, turned in this way, what is said of others as an accusation, when addressed to himself carries the implication of misfortune, as if Fate were being cursed. It is this attitude that helps give the song its strength and character. Out of the depths, not only of despair but also of human degradation, the singer maintains a fortitude and spirit that makes him sufficient unto himself, despite a full awareness of his predicament.

The unreliability of the printed versions stems from the origin of the song in the hands of its singer, W. G. Ross. It was his masterpiece and crowds flocked to hear

---

[1] Quoted by Christopher Pulling in *They Were Singing* from David Masson's *Memories of London in the Forties.*

him. Macqueen-Pope (whose grandfather saw Ross perform) has described the controlled terror and challenging bravado with which Ross entered. The refrain was hurled with furious venom at the audience and out of such abject squalor (and Ross was one of the few performers at that time who dressed in character appropriate to the act or song) emerged "a performance of high tragedy." The versions performed doubtless varied. Chance Newton had one he considered to be unprintable, although that might not mean very much for, writing in 1928, he felt it necessary to substitute a dash for "Damn" or "Blast" in the version he does quote.

Pope's suggestion of high tragedy may seem extravagant to those chary of using this phrase too freely. The song still has tremendous force and it combines terror and defiance, degradation and bitter courage, with that deep appeal inspired by the sight of a human being at bay like an animal. It is not that Sam Hall is ever noble: part of the song's strength lies in the fact that despite such *ignobility* he can, paradoxically, in a time of such anguish, reveal qualities we associate with man at his finest.

The indefiniteness of the versions must make the critic hesitant. The progression of tenses is vague, and I have thought it worth altering "I saw Molly" to the present. The underlying intention seems to be to take the audience with the singer in the terrible "So it's up the rope I go" (a line more metaphorically striking than factually exact) rather than to suggest that it is the dead and departed Hall looking back on the past. This vagueness may pass muster if it suggests the inability of the condemned man to express himself clearly, an inability as much a product of his character and lack of education as of the situation in which he finds himself. This is, then, not high tragedy in the Renaissance style, but a tragedy in miniature of low life, of the barely articulate; and it is the song's peculiar triumph that it gives articulate expression to the inarticulate.

Apart from its place in the development of the music hall, and its remarkable success in its own day (and apart from the interest it has in terms of human expression), this song has a further significance which it shares with all the music-hall songs that followed it. The singer addresses the audience directly. A trite enough comment, but one of great significance. In the music halls, as in all popular drama, the audience is spoken to directly—through the proscenium and across the footlights, if such luxuries exist. In legitimate, "fourth-wall" drama, the performance is across the stage, the audience "overhearing" what is enacted before them. "Sam Hall" (very much a dramatic song) was thus performed as was a Shakespearean soliloquy: directly to the audience. It is a technique still used by, say, a Jack Benny or a Frankie Howerd. Relatively recently modern dramatists have reverted to this technique. T. S. Eliot, in *Murder in the Cathedral*, was one of the first in our time. In this, the popular tradition has kept alive a valuable dramatic practice lost for generations in the legitimate theater.

Although "Sam Hall" was not Ross's only song, it was by far his greatest success. He began his working life as a compositor in Glasgow and turned from amateur singer to professional, gradually working his way south to London. Like so many popular performers of his time—indeed, of all times—in his last years he was destitute.

Champagne Charlie

Sung by George Leybourne. Words and music by Alfred Lee.
Version Copyright: 1925, Chapman and Hall.

COOL BURGUNDY BEN.

GEORGE LEYBOURNE.

FRANK W. GREEN ESQ.   ALFRED LEE.

MUSIC MAD.

GEORGE LEYBOURNE.   JAMES BAYMAN.

I've seen a deal of gaiety
   Throughout my noisy life,
With all my grand accomplishments
   I never could get a wife.
The thing I most excell in is
   The P.R. F.G. game,
A noise all night, in bed all day,
   And swimming in Champagne.

CHORUS:
For Champagne Charlie is my name,
Champagne Charlie is my game,
Good for any game at night, my boys,
Good for any game at night, my boys.
For Champagne Charlie is my name,
Champagne Charlie is my game,
Good for any game at night, my boys,
Who'll come and join me in a spree?

The way I gained my title's
   By a hobby which I've got
Of never letting others pay
   However long the shot;
Whoever drinks at my expense
   Are treated all the same,
From Dukes and Lords, to cabmen down,
   I make them drink Champagne.

From Coffee and from Supper Rooms,
   From Poplar to Pall Mall,
The girls, on seeing me, exclaim
   "Oh, what a Champagne Swell!"
The notion 'tis of everyone
   If 'twere not for my name,
And causing so much to be drunk,
   They'd never make Champagne.

Some epicures like Burgundy,
   Hock, Claret, and Moselle,
But Moet's vintage only
   Satisfies this Champagne swell.
What matter if to bed I go
   Dull head and muddled thick,
A bottle in the morning
   Sets me right then very quick.

Perhaps you fancy what I say
   Is nothing else but chaff,
And only done, like other songs
   To merely raise a laugh.
To prove that I am not in jest,
   Each man a bottle of Cham.
I'll stand fizz round, yes that I will,
   And stand it like a lamb.

CHAMPAGNE CHARLIE.

THE GREAT COMIC SONG WRITTEN & SUNG BY

GEORGE LEYBOURNE.

MUSIC BY
ALFRED LEE

PRICE 3/

Some years ago Ealing Film Studios endeavoured to recreate the atmosphere of the old music hall and the song they chose to name their film was "Champagne Charlie," with the comedian Tommy Trinder playing its singer, George Leybourne. Despite the considerable care taken to make the film accurate, it was not wholly convincing and I'm inclined to believe that a major difficulty was the song, "Champagne Charlie," and all that it implied. The choice was not in any obvious way a bad one. It made possible a centre of rivalry between Leybourne and Vance, the two great music-hall personalities of the time, and, in a way, the song was as typical as any single song could be of that period.

In his day George Leybourne, the original Lion Comique, typified the heavy swell, handsome, well- (if a little over-) dressed, befurred, and singing with great panache of the night life of a gay dog in London's West End. He presented, and "Champagne Charlie" typifies, a kind of dream existence—just conceivably possible (because Leybourne was paid to live the life about which he sang) but hardly within the reach of ordinary mortals. Not surprisingly this song set off a long succession of songs about drink, from Vance's "Clicquot" to Harry Clifton's "Barclay's Beer," described by its publishers as "an immense song." Immense or not, the song has passed away, but the beer is still for sale. On occasion, and given the support of the champagne merchants who considered it good advertising, Leybourne really did carry into life the promise of that last verse and stand champagne all around. His charm and generosity were real enough, but the particular *kind* of dream world he dispensed has largely lost its attraction for us. All that is left is the sense of panache and a rather engaging cheekiness (especially in the third verse). Has champagne any longer the magical appeal it evidently had for the mid-Victorians? To be a champagne swell, as Leybourne described it, might well have had an attraction for those whose necessity was as great, and whose horizons were as limited, as Robert Tressell asserted; but as our needs have changed, so have our dream worlds. Thus it is not the repetitiveness itself, nor the lack of wit, that makes a song such as "Champagne Charlie" so lacking in appeal now, but the particular *kind* of raffish excess it conjures up; we take our excesses differently now—or at least, we dream differently of them.

The tune retains its vigour; not for nothing was this devil's music adopted by the Salvation Army.[1] We have a not unlively glimpse of what seemed so desirable to our forebears; yet even in Leybourne's own day, a change was coming and his last song was mundane enough to be set in a teashop: "Ting, Ting, That's How the Bell Goes." It is not surprising that he lived in fits of abject depression towards his early end. As Macqueen-Pope laconically comments: "Maybe the tea killed him." And in a sense it did, for it killed one way of dreaming about life.

[1]Another music-hall song to be used by the Salvation Army was Alec Hurley's "I Ain't A-Going to Hell."

Villikins and His Dinah

Sung by Frederick Robson; Sam Cowell; J. L. Toole;
Muriel George and Ernest Butcher. Author and Composer Unknown.
Version Copyright: Ascherberg, Hopwood and Crew, Ltd.

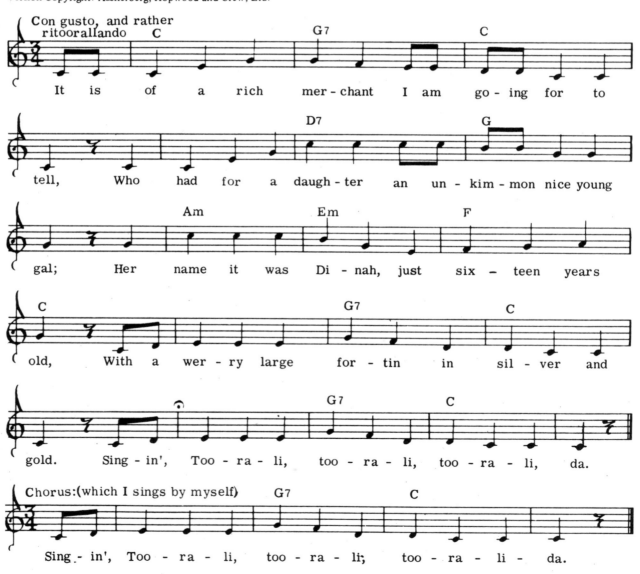

Con gusto, and rather ritooralfando

It is of a rich mer-chant I am go-ing for to tell, Who had for a daugh-ter an un-kim-mon nice young gal; Her name it was Di-nah, just six-teen years old, With a wer-ry large for-tin in sil-ver and gold. Sing-in', Too-ra-li, too-ra-li, too-ra-li, da.

Chorus:(which I sings by myself)

Sing-in', Too-ra-li, too-ra-li; too-ra-li-da.

NOTE: The word "Chorus" and the descriptions thereof, are spoken.

1. It is of a rich merchant I am going for to tell,
    Who had for a daughter an unkimmon nice young gal;
    Her name it was Dinah, just sixteen years old,
    With a werry large fortin in silver and gold.
    Singin', Too-ra-li, too-ra-li, too-ra-li-da.

    SPOKEN: *Chorus (Which I sings by myself):*

    Singin', Too-ra-li, too-ra-li, too-ra-li-da.

2. Now as Dinah was a-walking in the garding one day

    SPOKEN: *It was the front garding*

    The father comed up to her and thus to her did say:
    "Go dress yourself, Dinah, in gor-ge-us array,

    SPOKEN: *Take your hair out of paper*

    And I'll bring you home a hus-i-band both gal-li-ant and gay."
    Singin' . . .

    SPOKEN: *In favour of the parient's desire, and the wedding breakfast he
    was about to order of the pastrycook round the corner:*

    Too-ra-li . . .

3. SPOKEN: *Now this is what the daughter said to the prophetic parient in
    reply:*

    "Oh, father, dear father," the daughter she said,
    "I don't feel incli-ned to be mar-ri-ed;
    And all my large fortin I'll gladly give o'er,
    If you'll let me live single a year or two more."
    Singin' . . .

    SPOKEN: *Wheedling and persuasive chorus on behalf of the offspring's
    remonstrance to the author of her being:*

    Too-ra-li . . .

4. SPOKEN: *Now this here is what the paternal parient said agin to the
    daughter, and tells you what the parricidal papa parenthetically and pare-
    gorically pronounced, with all the parabolical particulars:*

    "Go, go boldest daughter," the parient replied,
    "If you don't feel incli-ned to be this young man's bride,

    SPOKEN CONFIDENTIALLY: *He was a merchant pieman from Abyssinia
    and exported baked taters to Timbuctoo for the Hottentots.*

    I'll give all your large fortin to the nearest of kin,
    And you shan't reap the benefit, not of one single pin,"
    Singin' (in a Californian tone), Too-ra-li . . .

SPOKEN: *Chorus of the enraged parient against his progeny:*

Too-ra-li . . .

5. SPOKEN: *Now this is the most melancholy part of it, and shows what the progeny was druv to in conskivence of the mangled obstropolosness and ferocity of the inconsiderable parient.*

Now as Villikins was a-walking the garding all round

SPOKEN: *It was the back garding this time.*

He spied his dear Dinah lying dead on the ground,
With a cup of cold pizen all down by her side,
And a billey-doo which said as 'ow 'twas by pizen she died.

SPOKEN: *The lable was marked, "British Brandy."*

Singin' . . .

SPOKEN: *Mournful and desponding chorus of the sympathizing sparrows, the sad and smoke-dried spectators of this malignant and misanthropic case of unfortunate severicide:* Too-ra-li . . .

6. *This here is what the lovyer did on the diskivery:*

Then he kissed her cold corper-ses a thousand times o'er,
And called her his dear Dinah, though she was no more;
Then he swallowed up the pizen, and sung a short stave—

SPOKEN: *Neither agreed with him*

And Villikins and his Dinah were laid in one grave.

Singin' (together), too-ra-li . . .

SPOKEN: *Dismal and duplicated chorus, in consequence of the double event:*

Too-ra-li . . .

MORI-AL

7. Now all you young men, don't you thus fall in love, nor
Do that not by no means disliked by your guv'nor;
And all you young maidens, mind who you claps your eyes on,
Think of Villikins and his Dinah—not forgetting the pizen.

Singin' . . .

SPOKEN: *Moral chorus, powerfully impressed:*

Too-ra-li . . .

(Extra verses recently recovered from the original Chaldean Manuscripts in the British Museum):

SPOKEN: *Now this is the superlatively supernatural wisitation which appeared to the parient at midnight, after the disease of his only progeny.*

8. At twelve the next night, by a tall poplar tree,
   The Ghost of Miss Dinah the parient did see,
   Arm in arm with her Villikins, and both looking blue;
   Said, "We shouldn't have been pizened if it hadn't been for you."

SPOKEN: *The two together in a quartet:*

Singin' . . .

SPOKEN: *Phantasmagorean and sepulchral chorus, to astonish the weak nerves of the parient.*

First and Second Voices: Singin' . . .

9. *The parient's fate and what he thought he would do, but didn't*

   Now the parient was struck with the horror of home,
   So he packed up his portmanteau, all round the world to roam.
   But as he was starting, he was seized with a shiver,
   Which shook him to pieces, and ended him for iver.

SPOKEN: *And those who come to pick up the bits could only sing:*

Too-ra-li . . .

SPOKEN: *Sympathetic chorus for the parient's fragments, though the verdict was, "Sarved him right."*

Too-ra-li . . .

10. SPOKEN: *Now, this not a comic song, you will observe, so we will take a return ticket back again to the subject and finish with:*

ANOTHER MORI-AL — NUMBER TWO

Now the moral is this — number one is not reckoned—
So this is the first moral, though it comes second:
You may learn from my song, which is true, every word,
All this wouldn't have happened — if it hadn't occurred.

SPOKEN: *And there would have been no excuse for singin'*

Too-ra-li . . .

SPOKEN: *Nor for the comprehensive and categorically conclusive chorus of:*

Too-ra-li, too-ra-li, too-ra-li-da.

With "Villikins and his Dinah" we enter the music-hall age, but the song itself came into prominence some ten years before the Canterbury opened its doors when it was sung by Frederick Robson at the Grecian Saloon and the Olympic Theater. (The Grecian adjoined the Eagle Tavern, which is referred to in "Pop Goes the Weasel.") It was taken up by Sam Cowell, who sang it first at Evans's Supper Rooms and then at the Canterbury, where he was Morton's first comic star.

Robson was regarded in his day as a master of lightning changes from side-splitting comedy to heart-rending pathos, although Christopher Pulling quotes Sir Henry Irving as saying that Robson "was great enough to know that he could only be great for three minutes." Nevertheless, any actor capable of making such transitions was at that time said to be "Robsonian."

Cowell also was originally an actor and had sung in opera. A scene from a burlesque version of *La Sonnambula* (in the serious version of which he had appeared) formed the central illustration of the cover to a collection of his comic songs. His acting capabilities were such that he successfully gave full evening entertainments on his own in London and New York. A third actor who worked in music hall and the legitimate theater, J. L. Toole, also sang "Villikins" and also gave solo entertainments. For two reasons, I have deliberately drawn attention to these actors, all noted in their day for their appearance in legitimate and popular drama, and who all sang "Villikins" and similar songs such as "Lord Lovell" and "The Ratcatcher's Daughter," and Toole's "Norrible Tale or The Suicidal Family." First, it is important to bear in mind that in many music-hall songs, action went with the words and music and this was essential to a full and vivid performance. Secondly, in songs like "Villikins," though the element of burlesque is strong (burlesque being very popular at the time), the capacity to make Robsonian changes—swift transitions to and from the comic and the pathetic—was an essential part of the performance. Furthermore the audiences had the capacity to react appropriately and, as will be apparent from a number of songs, this capacity has important implications. Thus the slightly whimsical, single-toned performance to which we are accustomed of songs like "Villikins," though not unpleasant, gives a simplified, watered-down version of the song, without realising its potentialities.

"Villikins" demands of an audience something of that Elizabethan capacity for multiconscious enjoyment described by S. L. Bethell in *Shakespeare and the Popular Dramatic Tradition*. There is, plainly, a conscious detachment at times that makes it possible to guy the song itself as it proceeds. This is apparent from the spoken asides, particularly those that comment on earlier asides as does "It was the back garding this time" and in the introduction of a second "Mori-al"

> Now the moral is this—number one is not reckon'd
> So this is the first moral, though it comes second.

It is also to be seen in the relish with which the name of the poison is mentioned —"British Brandy." This must be uttered slowly and solemnly with a slight pause between the two words so that the full implication of the horror can be communicated (especially to an audience aware of the peculiar implication of *British* brandy).

Such comments as these assume a relationship between singer and audience that is not to be found in the legitimate theater, and the technique undercuts the attempt to sustain a pathetic tone throughout the song. Nevertheless I am sure that to give the song its full due, the pathetic elements ought to be presented with such momentary intensity as the frequent undercutting irony will permit. The

24

kind of fluctuation required can be seen in the fifth verse. It is preceded by the kind of comically extravagant language associated with music-hall chairmen. The first line of the song should, when acted well, swiftly change the mood to tense anticipation. This may seem an absurd demand, but it is not impossible, given an audience's capacity to respond rapidly to the performer. The spoken aside makes a swift transition to detachment (it ought not to arouse more than a wry laugh), and then at once a return is made to the mood evoked by the first line of the verse. The actor's skill (and the audience's capacity) lies in not losing the mood engendered by the first line, despite the detached amusement of the aside. Thus, though the overall tone here is comic, for a brief moment the audience is made intensely conscious of the full implication of "lying dead on the ground." In this way a momentary pathetic intensity is created which, with the comedy and the detachment, makes for a complex sequence of emotions—of, indeed, a simultaneity of conflicting emotions: comedy and pathos, involvement and detachment. The context of Irving's comment on Robson's capacity is now clear.

It is easy and not unnatural to see "Villikins" and songs like it as demanding simple guying. But there is here, in an extremely bold form, the relationship of comic and pathetic which is used so skilfully by Albert Chevalier and which is to be found in some of Vesta Victoria's and Gus Elen's songs. It is not only an important relationship but also a precious one, as Samuel Beckett and Harold Pinter have shown recently in the legitimate theatre.

Sam Cowell

A Motto For Every Man

Sung by Harry Clifton and written by him. Music by Charles
Coote. Arranged by M. Hobson. Copyright Ascherberg,
Hopwood and Crew, Ltd.

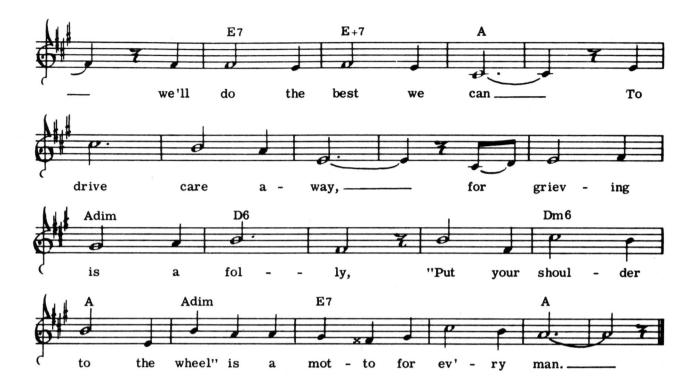

we'll do the best we can ____ To drive care a - way, ____ for griev - ing is a fol - ly, "Put your shoul - der to the wheel" is a mot - to for ev' - ry man. ____

Some people you've met in your time no doubt,
  Who never look happy or gay
I'll tell you the way to get jolly and stout,
  If you'll listen a while to my lay
I've come here to tell you a bit of my mind,
  And please with the same if I can.
Advice in my song you will certainly find,
  And a "motto for every man."

CHORUS:
So we will sing and banish melancholy,
  Trouble may come, we'll do the best we can
To drive care away, for grieving is a folly,
  "Put your shoulder to the wheel" is a motto
  for ev'ry man.

We cannot all fight in this *Battle of Life*,
  The weak must go to the wall.
So do to each other the thing that is right,
  For there's room in this world for us all.
"Credit refuse" if you've *"money to pay*,"
  You'll find it the wiser plan.
"And a penny lay by for a rainy day"
  Is a motto for every man.

A coward gives in at the first repulse,
  A brave man struggles again
With a resolute eye and a bounding pulse,
  To battle his way amongst men.
For he knows he has one chance in his time,
  To better himself if he can.
"So make your hay while the sun doth shine"
  That's a motto for every man.

Economy study but don't be mean,
  A penny may lose a pound.
Thro' this world a conscience clean,
  Will carry you safe and sound.
It's all very well to be free I will own,
  To do a good turn when you can,
But *"Charity always commences at home,"*
  That's a motto for every man.

Harry Clifton

Harry Clifton in a short life achieved great popularity in the supper rooms, music halls, and the more genteel world of provincial recitals designed for those to whom the music hall was anathema. He wrote over five hundred songs, of which undoubtedly the most famous is "Pretty Polly Perkins" (see "Cushie Butterfield"). In his day he was famed for his motto songs, of which three of the best-known are "Paddle Your Own Canoe," "Pulling Hard Against the Stream," and "Work, Boys, Work and Be Contented." His handsome but rather parsonical countenance can still be seen gazing, full of moral concern, from the covers of old copies of his songs. In his recital tours with his wife, he gained great if genteel success, and it is not without curiosity that the kind of songs he sang then could also draw tears in the music halls. Many of Clifton's songs were set to the waltzes of Charles Coote, then the proprietor of Hopwood and Crew, the house which published his songs. The melody of the chorus of "A Motto for Every Man" is adapted from "The Corn Flower Waltz."

If his motto songs drew approving nods in the Victorian drawing room and acclamation in the halls, they were to be seen in a different light a little later by Robert Tressell. In his novel, *The Ragged Trousered Philanthropists*, he describes

28

the singing of one of these motto songs at a works beano set in Mugsborough (Hastings) in 1906. Tressell died of tuberculosis in 1911, and his novel gives a grim account of the other side of the "good old days" in England prior to 1914. This song, says Tressell, "is the Marseillaise of the Tariff Reform Party, voicing as it does the highest ideals of the Tory workmen of this country":

> Now I'm not a wealthy man,
> But I lives upon a plan
> Wot will render me as 'appy as a King;
> And if you will allow, I'll sing it to you now,
> For time you know is always on the wing.

(Note the introduction of a motto and the implied invitation to sing the song, something which is common in Clifton's songs and found in a number of music-hall songs, including one of Lauder's given later in the volume.)

> Work, boys, work and be contented
> So long as you've enough to buy a meal.
> For if you will but try, you'll be wealthy—bye and bye—
> If you'll only put yer shoulder to the wheel.

The "bye and bye" is sardonically placed between dashes here. Tressell comments:

> That was all they wanted—to be allowed to work like brutes for the benefit of other people. They did not want to be civilized themselves and they intended to take good care that the children they had brought into the world should never enjoy the benefits of civilization either.

Half a century later, Macqueen-Pope in his book on the music hall, *The Melodies Linger On,* advocated the revival of "Work, Boys, Work and Be Contented."

The motto songs purvey a particularly odious form of superficiality, but they were certainly sincerely sung and sincerely heard in their time. Who, looking at Clifton's solemn features, can doubt that he meant what he wrote and sang? Nor can we doubt that those who listened felt, despite the manifold confusions of thought in the songs, that they were grasping a firm and meaningful truth. This substitute of superficial assumptions for thought-out truths is well illustrated by the second and third verses of "A Motto." The first four lines of the second verse were chosen to adorn the cover of this "serio-comic" song and the sentiments of the third verse are still with us, for they underlie a certain kind of television advertising.

To be fair to Clifton (not that I doubt his own sincerity) it might be worth quoting from one of his successful non-motto songs, "The Weepin' Willer." The last line of each verse is followed by a spoken modifier— for example: "P.S. Please excuse bad spelling – SPOKEN: *Orthography.*" In the penultimate stanza the deserted Miller's daughter is contemplating suicide:

> She looked at the Willer above,
> And said, "I'll hang in my garter,
> But what a mistake if the garter break,
> I shall be drown'd in the water."
> She look'd at the water below
> And her nerves began to totter,
> "I'm not very bold and I may take cold,
> I'll wait till the weather is hotter." [*spoken*] Milder

Oh Vladimir and Estragon!

Cushie Butterfield

Words by George Ridley; Music from Harry Clifton's
"Pretty Polly Perkins"; Arranged by C. E. Catcheside-Warrington.
Version Copyright: 1927, J. G. Windows, Ltd.

Moderato

Aa's a brok-en hair-ted keel-man and As's ower heed in luv Wiv a

young lass in Gyet-sid and Aa caall her me duv. Hor——

nyem's Cush-ie—— But-ter-field and she sells yal-la clay, And her
big lass an' a bon-nie lass an'—— she likes her beor, An' they

Chorus:

cous-in—— is a muck-man and they caall 'im Tom Gray.
caall her Cush-ie But-ter-field an' aa wish she was heor. She's a heor.

Aa's a broken hairted keelman and As's ower heed in luv
Wiv a young lass in Gyetsid and Aa caall hor me duv.
Hor nyem's Cushie Butterfield and she sells yalla clay,
And her cousin is a muckman and they caall 'im Tom Gray.

CHORUS:
She's a big lass an' a bonnie lass an' she likes hor beor,
An' they caall hor Cushie Butterfield and Aa wish she was heor.

Hor eyes is like two holes in a blanket bornt throo,
An' hor broos iv a mornin' wad spyen a yung coo,
An' when Aa heer hor shoutin' — "Will ye buy ony clay?"
Like a candyman's trumpet, it steals me yung hart away.

Ye'll oft see hor doon at Sangit when the fresh harrin comes in,
She's like a bagfull o' saadust tied roond wiv a string;
She weers big galoshes tee, an' hor stockins once was white,
An' hor bedgoon it's laelock, an' hor hat's nivver strite.

When Aa axed hor te marry us, she started te laff;
"Noo, nyen o' you monkey tricks, for Aa like nee sic chaff."
Then she started a' bubblin' an' roared like a bull,
An' the cheps on the Keel ses Aa's nowt but a fyuel.

She ses the chep 'et gets us 'ill heh te work ivvery day,
An' when he comes hyem at neets he'll heh to gan an' seek clay.
An' when he's away seekin't Aa'll myek baals an' sing,
O weel may the keel row that ma laddie's in.

Music hall was not confined to London. There was a very lively and often idiosyncratic provincial tradition and in some parts of Britain this was particularly strong. Many provincial performers migrated to London and although some adopted a neutral, or even a Cockney, line, many kept their provincial or national characteristics, as did George Formby from Lancashire, Tom Foy from Yorkshire, Harry Lauder and Will Fyffe from Scotland, and, of course, many Irish singers.

In some areas local traditions were strong. They retained their local individuality and their association with the public house was closer and has continued after the decline of the music halls. One such area was that between the rivers Wear and Tyne. Sometimes such movement as there was flowed from London instead of to it, local writers taking up tunes which had been made popular there and putting their own words to them. Two of the best writers from Tyneside were

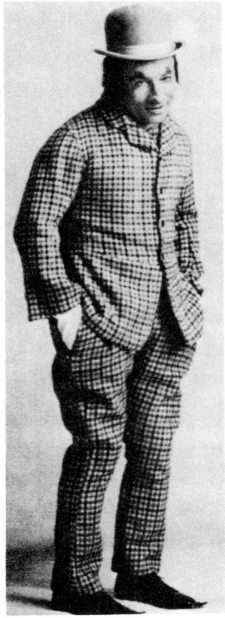

Tom Foy   Will Fyffe

George Ridley, who wrote "Blaydon Races" in 1862 as well as "Cushie Butterfield," and Joe Wilson, the author of "Keep Yor Feet Still, Geordie Hinney." The third song I have chosen is by Tommy Armstrong, better known as a Durham coalfield ballad writer, but whose "Wor Nanny's a Mazer" is in the music-hall tradition. All these songs are associated with bar-room singing and are part of a popular tradition that precedes (and continues on after) the music-hall proper.

"Cushie Butterfield" is set to the tune arranged by Harry Clifton for his "Pretty Polly Perkins of Paddington Green," but the words are far removed from those appropriate to that gentle lass. Ridley's song has tremendous vigour and is full of irony. He sketches his picture of Cushie with great economy. That the object of the keelman's adoration should be called his "duv" may give the appearance at first of the language of sophisticated verse that has gone down in the world, but the kick follows swiftly when it is flatly stated that this is a dove that sells "yalla clay" and that her cousin is a muckman. The description of Cushie in the second and third verses is vivid, particularly the depiction of her waiting for the herring, tied up like a sack of sawdust, wearing huge galoshes, dirty stockings, hat askew; but—and this is so ironically thrown in—she has also a bedgown of lilac. The sharpness and the economy with which Ridley reveals another aspect of this remarkably inelegant lass is astonishing. Up until this point there had seemed nothing to recommend her in the terms of conventional love songs, but her lilac bedgown suggests a more intriguing aspect than that implied by someone with a voice like a candyman's (a bailiff's) trumpeting. The suggestion of sexuality is brief but, in its isolation, striking.

Unlike the chorus of so many music-hall songs, this one has a significant relationship to the pattern of the whole song as well as being easily memorable (an essential of music-hall choruses). As noted, Ridley uses the techniques of deflation—the dove who sells yellow clay—and this is carried through in the first line of the chorus: big and bonnie, and, alliteratively, liking beer. (What worlds we are away from Pretty Polly and Champagne Charlie!) In the second line of the chorus this movement is reversed. The singer's yearning for Cushie is made the stronger by contrast because we now move towards intensification of feeling instead of (as in the earlier patterns of movement) towards deflation. Furthermore despite her outward unprepossessingness, the singer's plaintive longing persuades us that there is something more to Cushie than first sight suggests.

In the fourth verse we have Cushie's mixed reaction to the keelman's proposal of marriage. When I first heard the song I took her reaction to be laughter followed by anger, but there is nothing so simple about Miss Butterfield. It is evidently a laugh of uncertainty rather than scorn, for she turns to crying (and one version has the much less striking "blubbin") and her roaring suggests pent-up emotion as well as sheer volume. Once again Ridley achieves a nice juxtaposition.

The last verse is a trifle disappointing. It begins well enough with Cushie, back in form, outwardly showing her uncompromising demeanour, but the last two lines are inadequate. Once again there is a suggestion of a softer side to Cushie, but there is a lack of vividness. The title of the old song does not adequately express her feelings. It is so conventional that her attitude is obscure.

The strength of "Cushie Butterfield" as a song does not lie simply in the dialect in which it is written, although that gives a vigour of its own. What makes it so telling is, first of all, that it is written from within the life of which it speaks. Secondly, it does more than describe; it attempts, with some success, to assess the paradoxical qualities of this lass, outwardly so tough and ungainly, but who is not without complexity and even mystery.

Wotcher 'Ria

Sung by Bessie Bellwood and Nelly Farren. Written by Will Herbert and
Composed by Bessie Bellwood; Arranged by George Ison.
Copyright: Ascherberg, Hopwood and Crew, Ltd.

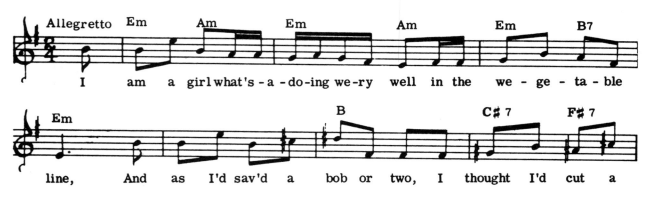

Allegretto Em Am Em Am Em B7

I am a girl what's-a-do-ing we-ry well in the we-ge-ta-ble

Em B C# 7 F# 7

line, And as I'd sav'd a bob or two, I thought I'd cut a

shine. So I goes and buys some tog - ger - y, These 'ere we - ry clothes you

see, And with the mon - ey I had left I thought I'd have a

spree. So I goes in - to a mus - ic hall where I'd oft - en been a -

fore, I don't go in the gal - ler - y but on the bot - tom

floor; I sits down by the Chair - man and calls for a pot of

Stout, My pals in the gal - ler - y spot - ted me, and they all com - menced to

Chorus:

shout Wot - cher 'Ri - a? 'Ri - a's on the job, Wot - cher

'Ri - a? Did you spec - u - late a bob? Oh, 'Ri - a she's a toff and she

looks im - men - si - koff, And they all shout - ed, Wot - cher 'Ri - a?

I am a girl what's doing wery well in the wegetable line,
And as I'd saved a bob or two, I thought I'd cut a shine.
So I goes and buys some toggery, these 'ere wery clothes you see,
And with the money I had left I thought I'd have a spree.
So I goes into a music hall where I'd often been afore,
I don't go in the gallery but on the bottom floor;
I sits down by the Chairman and calls for a pot of Stout,
My pals in the gallery spotted me and they all commenced to shout—

CHORUS:
Wotcher 'Ria? 'Ria's on the job
Wotcher 'Ria? Did you speculate a bob?
Oh, 'Ria she's a toff
And she looks immensikoff,
And they all shouted, Wotcher 'Ria?

Of course I chaffed them back again, but it worn't a bit of use.
The poor old Chairman's baldie head they treated with abuse;
They threw an orange down at me, it went bang inside a pot,
The beer went up like a fountain, and a toff copt all the lot;
It went slap in his chevy, and it made an awful mess,
But what gave me the needle was, it spoilt me blooming dress.
I thought it was getting rather warm, so I goes towards the door,
When a man shoves out his gammy leg, and I fell smack on the floor.

SPOKEN: *I turned round and spoke to him wery politely. I said,
"What cher want to go and shove your jolly old gammy leg out like that
that for?" He said, "I beg your pardon, Madam." I says, "Beg
nothing, you jolly old josser!" He says, "Don't you be saucy
or I shall get you chucked out." When my pals spot I'm having
a row, and they see the old man has got a wooden leg, they shout
out, "Wotcher! Half a man and half a tree?!"*

Chorus

Now the gent that keeps the Music Hall he patters to the bloke,
Of course they blamed it all on me, but I couldn't see the joke.
So I upped and told the governor as how he'd shoved me down,
And with his jolly old wooden leg, tore the frilling off my gown.
But law bless you! It worn't a bit of use, the toff was on the job.
They said, "Outside!" and out I went, and they stuck to my bob.
Of course I left so wild, to think how I'd been taken down,
Next time I'll go in the gallery with my pals, you bet a crown.

SPOKEN: *You don't catch me going chucking my money away, trying
to be a toff any more — the way they served me wasn't so very
polite. They brought the chucker-out and he said, "Come on,
'Ria, you've been kicking up a pretty row," he says, "Come
on, outside." I says, "Shan't, shan't! There you are!
Shan't!!" He took hold of me and handed me out, just as
though I'd been a sack of taters. When I got outside, my
young man was waiting. So he says, "Serves you jolly well
right, 'Ria! You shouldn't try to be a lady, 'cause it
don't suit yer." Just then my pals were coming out of the
gallery and they all commenced shouting:*
Chorus

36

Bessie Bellwood was one of the first of the great women characters of the music halls; and she was the kind of woman who epitomised the spirit of the halls. She had a magnificent gift of repartee, she could dominate a lively audience, and with her courage and humour went a deep generosity that became a byword. This was not limited to giving money to those out of luck; but, as Chance Newton has recorded, like Florence St. John and Marie Lloyd, she would "perform the most menial, most trying, and painful offices for the needy, sick, and dying."

In this, her best-known song, there is something of the character of the music halls in the days when they still had chairmen—and something too of her own spirit, although she presents herself as a visitor and, more ironically, as one defeated in argument, a fate almost unknown to Bessie Bellwood. Thus, when she sang the song, it would have for audiences of her day an amusing incongruity; a little of this self-deflationary character is still apparent.

It could be argued that, in its original context, because sung by so indomitable a character, the quality of the self-deflation was to be taken ironically, whereas the song as it stands (without reference to the characteristics of the singer, or anything else outside the song) is in the self-deflationary popular dramatic tradition.

Through this self-deflation a lively but attractive "slice of life" is seen from within that life. 'Ria is doing well in vegetables, just as Bessie in her former life as Kathleen Mahoney may occasionally have done well as a rabbit puller in the East End of London. 'Ria is very self-conscious that she is stepping out, not merely in the sense of stepping out for an evening, but also overstepping those indefinable but rigid boundaries that confine her to a particular way of life; and it is her own friends as well as the toffs who make her attempt to step briefly into another kind of society impossible. It would be silly to be portentous about 'Ria's ejection from the floor of the hall, but the fact that she doesn't fit is the theme of the song.

It is significant that though she behaves with decorum—and she comically proves the fitness of her dress for the occasion by directing the audience's attention to "these wery clothes you see"—it is everyone else who makes her position intolerable. There is, too, a subtle—perhaps, a sly—difference between the reactions of those in the gallery and those on the floor of the hall. Her friends up aloft still see her as one of them, and though she chaffs them back (and "chaff" gives the right tone of jolly teasing, as well as being, for an audience of the time, a delightful understatement of Bessie's power of repartee), their horseplay makes it too warm for her so she begins to beat a discreet retreat. It is then that we have the pointed contrast between the behaviour of friends and toffs. The blame for the incident is put squarely onto 'Ria, and so she is ejected with a torn and stout-stained dress—but no shilling. No wonder she felt wild at being so taken down.

It is a comic song, yet in the song and the patter, the conflict of the classes is sharply presented. This is not to be seen in the deliberate tripping — as much a joke as the orange in the pot of beer, doubtless—but in what follows. 'Ria's "wery politely" is ironical. It doesn't take much imagination to guess at the vigour which animated "What cher want to go and shove your jolly old gammy leg out like that for?" But the old Josser's affected "I beg your pardon, Madam," and his threat to have her chucked out, compare unfavourably with 'Ria's righteous indignation. Not that her friends in the gallery help her case much with their "Wotcher! Half a man and half a tree!"

The moral is ironic. 'Ria's young man may be right: but is it because to be a lady amongst such toffs doesn't accord with the downright self-awareness of a 'Ria?

Like very many music-hall songs, "Wotcher 'Ria" has patter between the verses. In addition to extending the song and providing contrast, the patter often made for a better integration of the chorus, as in this song.

Although "What Cheer 'Ria" (to give it its usual spelling—"Wotcher" more accurately represents the sound) is a boisterous song originally sung by a very vigorous singer, it would be a mistake to present it too brashly. It is lively but it is also self-aware, and as with all stories that we tell against ourselves, the element of self-criticism should be apparent if the best is to be got out of the song or story. If this is clear, then the implied criticism of the toffs on the floor will be more telling and the song's potentialities will be more adequately realised.

He's Going To Marry Mary Ann

Sung by Bessie Bellwood. Written and Composed by Joseph Tabrar.
Copyright: Francis, Day & Hunter, Ltd.

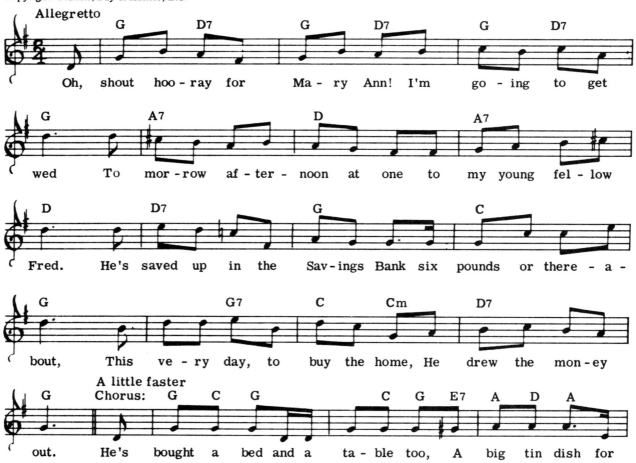

mak - ing stew, A large flat - iron to iron his shirt, And a flan - nel and a scrub-bing brush to wash a-way the dirt. And he's bought a pail and ba - sins three, A cof - fee pot, a ket - tle, and a tea-pot for the tea, And a soap-bowl and a la - dle, And a grid-iron and a cra - dle, And he's going to mar - ry Ma - ry Ann, that's me! He's going to mar - ry Ma - ry Ann!

Oh, shout hooray for Mary Ann!
　　I'm going to get wed
Tomorrow afternoon at one
　　To my young fellow, Fred.
He's saved up in the Savings Bank
　　Six pounds or thereabout,
This very day, to buy the home,
　　He drew the money out.

CHORUS:
He's bought a bed and a table too,
　　A big tin dish for making stew,
A large flatiron to iron his shirt,
　　And a flannel and a scrubbing brush to
　　wash away the dirt.
And he's bought a pail and basins three,
　　A coffee pot, a kettle, and a teapot for
　　the tea,
And a soap bowl and a ladle,
　　And a gridiron and a cradle,
And he's going to marry Mary Ann, that's *me!*
　　He's going to marry Mary Ann!

My friends remark, "Oh, what a lark
　　To see the money fly!"
They say we're two young sillies, and
　　We don't know what to buy.
But just you leave my Fred alone,
　　He's such a knowing sort,
He lays the money out A-1,
　　And this is what he's bought.

He went right off to Maples, where
　　The furniture is grand,
He said he meant to have things new,
　　Not common second-hand.
We've got one chair, one table, and
　　One chest of drawers, two mugs,
Two plates, two cups, two saucers, and
　　A pair of water-jugs.

Mary Ann appears in several songs but, unlike John Willie, who was always associated with George Formby Sr., she was the possession — or the possessor — of several singers. Mary Ann was after George Bastow and, much to Dan Leno's delight, she refused him in marriage. This song about Mary Ann was written by one of the most prolific of music-hall songwriters. According to Chance Newton and Christopher Pulling, Tabrar was the author of thousands, literally thousands, of songs. He wrote George Leybourne's last song, "Ting, Ting, That's How The Bell Goes," and he was still writing songs and putting on shows fifty years later, well after the First Great War. His most famous song, for which, like this one, he also wrote words and music, was Vesta Victoria's "Daddy Wouldn't Buy Me A Bow-wow." A song by his son, Fred Earle, is also printed in this collection.

There is nothing sentimental about this song; it is far too down-to-earth for that. The joyous delight in the occasion seems to be communicated even to those watching this extravagance—"Oh what a lark to see the money fly!"—and there is a sense of affectionate regard in the phrase, "two young sillies," which is the nearest the song gets to being sentimental.

It is noticeable that there is no mention of love or affection. The depths of Fred's feelings for Mary Ann are to be implied from his insistence that they shall have nothing "common second-hand" (and notice the rejection of "common," with its subtle suggestion of hierarchical refinements within the class structure). Mary Ann's delight is quite plain from the phrasing of the last lines of the chorus.

"He's Going To Marry Mary Ann" is not a great song. It boasts no complexities, though it gives a little insight into attitudes to love and marriage. What it has in abundance is unaffected gaiety.

Maples, incidentally, still flourishes.

The London Pavilion, 1885

Wor Nanny's a Mazer

Words by Tommy Armstrong to an old tune;
Arranged by C. E. Catcheside-Warrington.
Version Copyright: 1912, J. G. Windows, Ltd.

Allegro moderato

Wor Nan-ny an' me myed up wor minds te gan an' catch the train, ___
When __ we got te Row-lan's Gill the morn - in' train was gyen

Te gan te the toon te buy some claes for wor lit-tle Bil-ly an' Jane ___ But
An' thor was-n't an-other one gan' that way till sev-en-teen min-utes te

1. Jane ___ But one. ___
2. So Aa

ses te wor Nan "It's a long way te gan," an Aa saa biv hor fayce she wes vext.
gov a bit smile when Aa spoke up an' ses, "There's a pub - bi - lick hoose a-long heor,
Nan we se stoot __ Aa knew she'd not waak an' she did - n't seem will - in' te try.

But Aa ses, "Niv-vor mind we heh plen-ty o' time, we'll stop an' gan on wi' the next."
We'll gan a-long there an' get wor-sels warm an'a glass o' the best bit-ter beor."
When Aa think o' the trou-ble Aa'd wiv hor that day, Aa's like to borst oot __ an' cry.

She But

Chorus: And ay wor Nan-ny's a maz - er an' a maz - er she re - mains, ___ An' as
lang as Aa live Aa win-net for-get the day we lost the trains.

Wor Nanny an' me myed up wor minds te gan an' catch the train,
Te gan te the toon te buy some claes for wor little Billy an' Jane.
But when we got to Rowlan's Gill the mornin' train wes gyen
An thor wasn't another one gan' that way till siventeen minutes te one.
So Aa ses te wor Nan, "It's a lang way te gan," an Aa saa biv hor feyce she
   wes vext.
But Aa ses, "Nivvor mind we heh plenty o' time, we'll stop an' we'll gan on wi'
   the next."
She gov a bit smile when Aa spoke up an ses, "There's a pubblick hoose alang
   heor,
We'll gan along there an get worsels warm an' a glass o' the best bitter beor."
But Nan we se stoot Aa knew she'd not waak an' she didn't seem willin' te try.
When Aa think o' the trouble Aa'd wiv hor that day,
Aa's like te borst oot an' cry.

CHORUS:
And ay wor Nanny's a Mazer an' a mazer she remains,
An' as lang as Aa live Aa winnet forget the day we lost the trains.

So doon we went te the pubbilick hoose an' when we got te the door
She sez, "We'll gan in te the parlor end for Aa've niver been heor afore."
So in we went an' teuk wor seats, an' afore Aa rang the bell,
Aa axed hor what she wes gannin, te hev, an' she sez, "The syem as yorsel."
So Aa caalled for two gills of the best bittor beor: she paid for them when
   they come in.
An afore she'd swallied a half o' hors, she said, "Aa wad rethur hev gin."
So Aa caalled for a glass o' the best Hollands Gin, she swallied it doon the
   forst try.
Aa sez to wor Nan, "Thoo's as gud as a man." She sez, "Bob man, Aa feel
   varry dry."
So Aa caalled for another; that went the same way; Aa sez, "That'll settle
   thee thirst."
She sez, "Aa've had two, an' aa'm ne better noo,
Than Aa was when Aa swallied me first."

She sat an' she drank till she got tight; she sez, "Bob man, Aa feel varry queer."
Aa sez, "Thoo's had nine glasses o' gin te me two gills o' beor."
She lowsed hor hat an' then hor shaal an' hoyed them on the floor.
Aa thowt wor Nan we gan' wrang iv hor mind so Aa set mesel near the door.
She sez, "Give us order, Aa'll sing a bit sang." Aa sat an Aa glowered at hor;
Aa thowt she wes jokin' for Aa nivvor hard wor Nanny sing ony before.
She gave us a touch o' "The Row i' the Gutter," she pleased ivery one that
   wes there;
There wes nebody in but wor Nanny an' me; an' Aa laffed till me belly wes
   sair.
She tried te stand up te sing "The Cat Pie" but she fell doon an' myed sic a
   clatter,
She smashed fower chairs, an' the landlord come in an' sez, "What the deuce is
   the matter."

He sez te me, "Is this yor wife, an' where de ye belang?"
Aa sez, "It is, an' she's teun a fit wi' tryin' te sing a bit sang".
He flung his arms aroond hor waist, an' trailed hor ower the floor,
An poor aad Nan, like a dorty hoose cat, was hoyed oot side o' the door.
An' there she wes lyin', byeth groanin' an' cryin', te claim hor Aa really thowt
   shyem;

Aa tried ta lift hor, but Aa cudden't shift hor, an' Aa wished Aa had Nanny at
  hyem.
The papor man said he wad give hor a lift, se we hoisted hor in to the trap:
But Nan was that tight she cuddent sit up, so we fastened hor down wiv a strap.
She cuddent sit up an' she waddent lie doon, an' she kicked till she broke the
  conveyance.
She lost a new basket, hor hat an' hor shaal,
That wummin, wi' lossin' the trains.

A SELECTION OF VARIANTS

Catcheside-Warrington's text and that for the Topic recording differ (and indeed
the sung and printed Topic versions differ slightly); as with so many songs of
this kind, a single definitive text cannot be expected and many songs given in
a single version in this volume will show variants if compared with other versions. The Topic recording is sung to a different tune. Some of the more interesting variants are recorded below, the Catcheside-Warrington version (upon
which I have chiefly relied) being given first.

VERSE ONE:
Wor Nanny an' me / Now me an' wor Nan
Billy / Jimmy
stoot / fat
Aa's like te / If aa liked aa could

CHORUS:
And ay / An' it's eh
winnit / never

VERSE TWO:
a half o' hors / three parts of hor gill
"Aa wad" / "Bob, man, Aa wad"
swallied it doon / gobbled it up

The Melody Line (Topic Records) for lines 9,
10 and 11 varies from music on opposite page

VERSE THREE:
two gills / three gills
hoyed / tossed

The Melody Line (Topic Records) for lines 7,
and 8 varies from music on opposite page

VERSE FOUR:
trailed / hurled
poor aad Nan / Nan, poor sowl,
hoyed / tumbled
lift / ride
Nan was that tight . . . sit up / she wadn't
  sit up an' she wadn't lie doon.

Most of Tommy Armstrong's songs are ballads about life in the coalfields of Northumberland and Durham. Many recount pit disasters and the bitter struggle between the men and the pit masters, but a number are comic accounts of his own life (including a rumbustious description of his birth). One of Tommy Armstrong's best-known songs is this one in the music-hall or public-house style. It is included in one of the four volumes of Tyneside songs compiled by C.E. Catcheside-Warrington (to which I am indebted for the three Northumbrian songs printed here) and it has been recorded twice in the last year or two in two strikingly different versions in collections called "Songs Of The Tyne" (Delyse), where it is sung by Owen Brannigan, and "Tommy Armstrong Of Tyneside" (Topic), with Tom Gilfellon. Different tunes are used and the manners of presentation—one sophisticated and the other "natural"—the variant content of the versions, and even their different orthographies, take one back to the vagaries of the living tradition.

A full version of the song is given here and the words are spelled so that a reasonable interpretation of the sound may be arrived at while bearing in mind that many who read this text will not be familiar with even the most commonly heard English dialects. Some of the more interesting variations between the two versions mentioned (Delyse follows Catcheside-Warrington) are noted. The length and number of lines vary considerably, but the "melody" for the body of the song is such that it is not difficult to fit in any number of lines or syllables.

The song tells of a comic domestic disaster. Wor Nanny stands in relation to her husband as does Cushie Butterfield to her keelman. It is clearly she who holds the purse strings and though the husband does the ordering, it is the wife who calls the tune—to the extent of nine glasses of the best Hollands Gin to two (or possibly three) glasses of beer, although admittedly, the "best" bitter beer. In the days when the song was written, the men of this area liked to exert, at least outwardly, dominance over their wives. The tradition is dying hard but is still comically reflected in nostalgic retrospect in the popular newspaper strip of Andy Capp. Thus in Wor Nanny and Cushie Butterfield there is an interesting variation on accepted outward appearances. In this song the irony is that the dominant—nay, usurping—wife comes an almighty cropper.

The vividness with which the story is told is partly the result of the choice of verbs (although the variant versions make it difficult to be certain always which is intended where) and partly the accuracy of the description. To use the language of one school of literary critics, in this song a deeply felt experience is communicated. It is easy to sense the husband hastening to make the best of things when he sees "biv hor feyce she was vext," and it is possible to enjoy his minor success at the result of his suggestion: "She gove a bit smile," and to sense also the reluctant but deep-seated pleasure (attitudes very neatly hit off) she takes in passing the time away in the public house—not that she was accustomed to so spending "her" time, oh no! Even if we don't know the outcome of the song there is, for us, a delightful anticipation of trouble ahead for the redoubtable Nanny in her "The syem as yorsel," redolent with comfortable assurance. Throughout the song, dialect is not an imitation of how others speak but a true mimesis, an idiosyncratic and imaginative expression of this particular attitude to life. This can be seen not only in the distinctive choice of words but also in idiomatic expressions like "Aa really thowt shyem."

The husband's reactions in the longer version of the third verse are only sketchily described. The transition from glowering by the door to laughing till his belly is sore is made inadequately. The logic of the situation if further sacrificed for the sake of a laboured joke that Nanny pleased everyone there but that there was no one there but the two of them. If Nanny's behaviour before singing had proved embarrassing, then her giving voice in this fashion might be expected to be even more excrutiatingly anguishing. In the shorter version the husband's attitude is more consistent with the logic of the experience. It is not that in other circumstances the sight of Wor Nanny trying to give "a bit sang" might not excite her husband's laughter, but simply that it is not appropriate to the experience being realised in this song. The logic—the artistic logic, that is, not the logic of rational behaviour—demands that it is we who should laugh at Nanny, not that her husband should find her amusing.

The last verse provides a fitting end to the day and again the language is skill-fully chosen, from the squalid comparison with a dirty house cat to the mock-elegance of the word, "conveyance."

There is another quality about this song that ought to be mentioned. Husband and wife live in a curiously isolated world. The landlord and even the paper man seem outsiders, and we hever hear about who served all those glasses of gin. The very absence of the train suggests an empty world. The result, despite the vividness of the life depicted, is to give an air of unreality to the song as if we were in a world of make-believe. Is there just a touch of fantasy here? Is this what a wife-dominated husband might have dreamed? Or is this to suggest a subtlety unwarranted by the song?

Keep Your Feet Still, Geordie Hinney

Words by Joe Wilson; Tune: "Nellie Gray";
Arranged by C. E. Catcheside-Warrington.
Version Copyright: 1927, J. G. Windows, Ltd.

Moderato

Wor—— Geor-die and Bob John-son byeth lay i' one—— bed In a lit-tle lod-gin' hoose that's doon the shore. Be-fore he'd been an hour a-sleep a kick from Geor-die's fut Made him wak-en up te roar i' stead o' snore.

Chorus:

Keep yor feet still Geor-die Hin-ney let's be hap-py for the neet For Aa may not be se hap-py thro' the day. So give us that bit com-fort, Keep yor feet still Geor-die lad And—— div-vent drive me bon-ny dreams a-way.

Wor Geordie and Bob Johnson byeth lay i' one bed
In a little lodgin' hoose that's doon the shore.
Before he'd been an hour asleep a kick from Geordie's fut
Made him waken up te roar i'stead o' snore.

CHORUS:
Keep yor feet still Geordie hinney let's be happy for the neet
For Aa may not be se happy thro' the day.
So give us that bit comfort, keep yor feet still Geordie lad
And divvent drive me bonny dreams away.

Aa dremt thor wes a dancin' held an' Mary Clark wes there,
An' Aa thowt we tript it leetly on the floor,
An' Aa prest hor heevin' breest te mine when walsin' roond the room,
That's mair than Aa dor ivver de afore.

Ye knaa the lad she gans wi', they caall him Jimmy Green,
Aa thowt he tried te spoil us i' wor fun,
But Aa dremt Aa nailed 'im heavy, an' blacked the big feul's eyes,
If Aa'd slept its hard te tell what Aa wad deun.

Aa thowt Aa set hor hyem that neet; content we went alang,
Aa kissed hor lips a hundord times or mair,
An' Aa wisht the road wad nivvor end, se happy like was Aa,
Aa cud waak a thoosand miles we' Mary there.

Aa dreamt Jim Green had left the toon an' left he's luv te me,
An Aa thowt the hoose wes foonished wi' the best,
An Aa dremt Aa just hed left the Chorch wi' Mary be me side,
When yor clumsy feet completely spoilt the rest.

Joe Wilson's "Keep Yor Feet Still" is like "Cushie Butterfield" in that it is set to a well-known tune and is concerned with love. But if "Cushie Butterfield" is hardly conventionally romantic, "Keep Yor Feet Still" is even less so at first sight. The setting itself is the reverse of romantic—two lads sharing a bed for the night in a little lodging house, with all the discomfort that that entails made very apparent.

There is a structural weakness in that in the first verse the narrator is neither Bob Johnson nor "Wor Geordie," although in the remaining verses Bob tells the story. As with "Cushie Butterfield" the chorus is an integral part of the structure of the song. It not only serves to remind us of the rather sordid down-to-earthness of the situation, but its appearance forms part of a logical sequence in the broken dreams that form the "second subject" of the song, as it were. Throughout there is a contrast between a real and a dream world which makes for tension within the song.

This tension is carried through by the language itself. Apart from not driving Bob's bonny dreams away, there is also the contrast between being "happy for the neet" and the lesser likelihood of being happy "thro' the day" (and "thro'" is a much more telling preposition here than "in" would be).

By contrast the dream recounts four sharply defined cameos, incidents in a successful dream courtship of Mary Clark—dancing with her, disposing of her rival ("the big feul"), seeing Mary home, and, having set up house, marrying her. Like "Cushie Butterfield" this is done with great vividness and economy, and yet (largely by the skilful use of the chorus) there is no absurd sense of haste. The dream is presented as larger than life but with an attractive humour. We know less of Mary Clark than of Geordie's feet, except for that expressive phrase, "prest hor heevin' breast," which contrasts amusingly if conventionally with the tripping lightly in the waltz. And as Bob says, it's more than he ever dared do before. The last line of the third verse has a nice sense of ambiguity. Is it a vain boast that he might have given Jimmy Green an even more comprehensive hiding? Or is Bob a little doubtful upon awakening as to what more he could have done? The line carries both senses and, at the same time, neatly juxtaposes the two worlds of the song.

The second and fourth verses are entirely concerned with the dream world. In the third verse, although there is this reference to wakening, it is expressed negatively—"If Aa'd slept"—and the point of reference is the dream world. Thus each "dream" is shattered by the chorus—that is, by Geordie's feet—until we get to the last verse. Here there is a slight but very effective variation. In this verse we are told the final dramatic instalment of this dream romance in its first three lines. Then the last line of the verse, instead of completing the dream, returns sharply to a forceful complaint against Geordie's feet. This anticipates the chorus and very effectively the pattern of the song is broken. As the line succinctly puts it, those feet have "completely spoilt the rest." Apart from the element of surprise here, the dream-then-chorus pattern is broken in a way that acts out the event itself. There is another structural advantage, too, for the final chorus, repeating as it does what we know from the last line of verse five, serves as a coda to the whole.

Like so many pub and music-hall songs, "Keep Yor Feet Still" is very much a product of the way of life that has produced it. It presents this life without apology or any false sense of values. It accepts as part of that way of life what, in more sophisticated songs, would doubtless be a cause for sniggering—the two lads in one bed. Yet the fact of the two lads together (stemming as it does from the life of the time) is not only the cause of the song in the sense that it is the proximity of Geordie's wretched feet that provides the chorus, it is also, surely, the cause of the dream, of the train of subconscious thought—compare Iago's assertion regarding Cassio in *Othello* (3.3.414f). Here lies the song's central (and very natural) irony: if only Geordie were Mary, then the feet would make for a happier disturbance.

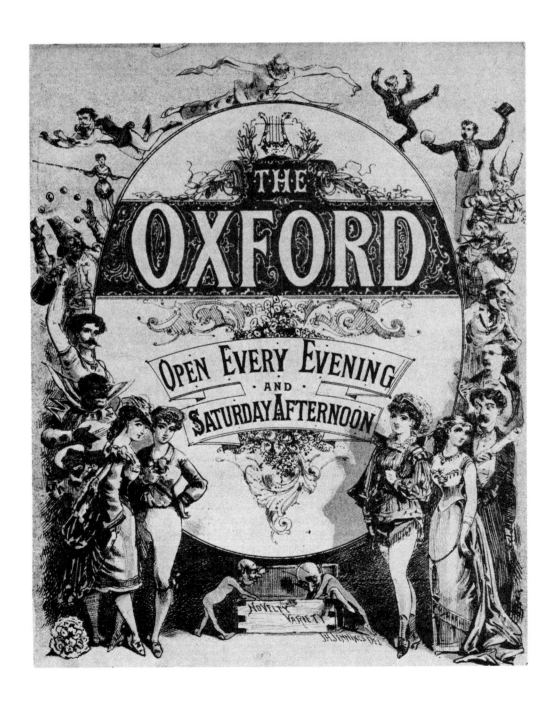

Don't Go Out To-night, Dear Father

Words by M. E. Golding; Music by W. L. Thompson.
Version Copyright: 1925, Chapman and Hall.

Moderato with feeling

Don't go out to-night, dear fa-ther, Don't re-fuse this once I pray;

Tell your com-rades mo-ther's dy-ing, Soon her soul will pass a-way;

Tell them, too, of dar-ling Wil-lie, Him we all so much do love,

How his lit-tle form is droop-ing Soon to bloom a-gain a-bove.

Chorus:

Don't go out to-night, dear fa-ther; Think, oh think, how sad 'twill be

When the an-gels come to take her, Pa-pa won't be there to see.

The very great scamps like pretty songs, and are melted by them; so are honest people.
—Thackeray

Don't go out to-night, dear father,
    Don't refuse this once, I pray;
Tell your comrades mother's dying,
    Soon her soul will pass away; .
Tell them, too, of darling Willie,
    Him we all so much do love,
How his little form is drooping
    Soon to bloom again above.

CHORUS:
Don't go out to-night, dear father;
    Think, oh think, how sad 'twill be
When the angels come to take her,
    Papa won't be there to see.

Tell me that you love dear mamma,
    Lying in that cold, cold room,
That you don't love your comrades better,
    Cursing there in that saloon.
Oh, dear father, do not leave us,
    Think, oh think, how sad 'twill be,
When the angels come to take her,
    Papa won't be there to see.

Morning found the little pleader
    Cold and helpless on the floor,
Lying where he madly struck her
    On that chilly night before;
Lying there, with hands uplifted,
    Feebly uttering words of prayer;
Heavenly Father, please forgive him,
    Reunite us all up there.

51

Temperance songs, of which "Don't Go Out To-night, Dear Father" is one of the best known, hardly seem appropriate to the atmosphere of the music hall; and yet, 79 years after it was written in 1886, "Please Sell No More Drink To My Father" was still being sung in a London "olde-tyme" variety show. Like the ever-running play, "The Drunkard," temperance songs offer a perverse delight very different from the sober instruction their authors intended.

Nevertheless it would be a mistake to assume that, in their hey-day, they could not be sung and received in a mood of deep seriousness. It is far from easy in any later age to imagine that the sentimental, the melodramatic, and the extravagantly violent of an earlier age, could have been taken seriously, and even by the aesthetically sophisticated. For a brief time in their own period these forms of artistic excess give precise expression to something in that age, and, provided their craftsmanship is sound, they can be taken seriously in their own time.

Their prime weakness is not a lack of aesthetic, moral, or intellectual strength, though all these may be found wanting. Their weakness, paradoxically, is what gives them their peculiar strength on their first appearance: their capacity to accord so exactly with something relevant to their age. So bound up are they with their own age that they have little capacity to be meaningful, in their original style, in any other period. Plays such as "Philaster" and "The Maid's Tragedy" are more "serious" than many critics imagine. Their authors, Beaumont and Fletcher, gave precise expression to something in their age, narrow though it was in its concern. But what was so appropriate in the time of James I has never been so precisely appropriate again, and it is in the more complex concerns, the more widely diffused interests of Shakespeare's plays, that later generations have found significance—from burlesque to Freud. We cannot take "The Maid's Tragedy" fully "seriously" any more than we can take "Don't Go Out To-night, Dear Father," but that should not make us imagine that in their day they could not be received seriously by even the aesthetically sophisticated. At the turn of the century—or even in ten years' time—will it not be found difficult to believe that the sentimentality and violence of "Look Back in Anger" were taken "seriously" by so many people in 1956?

What is perhaps even more surprising is that, in addition to being taken seriously, such songs as "Don't Go Out" were simultaneously being parodied, and enjoyed "seriously" and as parodies by the same audiences (but see the commentary to "At My Time Of Life").

"Don't Go Out" and "Please Sell No More Drink" represent only one kind of a large group of Victorian songs which deal with morbid subjects, especially songs which delight in the demise of delicate damsels. Willson Disher quotes a delightful example, a lament for Lilly Dale. This so moved Trollope (rather supporting what has just been said about such compositions being taken seriously in their own age) that he gave the name Lily Dale to a favourite heroine (of the novel "The Small House At Allington"). The second verse and chorus may suggest what was so aesthetically pleasing in 1864:

> Her cheeks, that once glowed with the rose tint of health,
> By the hand of disease had turned pale,
> And the death damp was on the pure white brow
> Of my poor lost Lilly Dale.
>
> Oh! Lilly, sweet Lilly,
> Dear Lilly Dale,
> Now the wild rose blossoms o'er her little grave,
> 'Neath the trees in the flowering vale.

In several temperance songs we are told of the death of a sickly child while father is out drinking. Quite often the dying child makes a pathetic, loving reference to his erring father, as in another gem quoted by Willson Disher:

> Father, dear father, come home with me now,
> The clock in the steeple strikes three [1]
> The house is so lonely, the night is so long
> For poor weeping mother and me.
> Yes, we are alone for Benny is dead,
> And gone to the angels of light,
> And these were the very last words that he said,
> "I want to kiss Papa good night."
> Come home, come home, oh father, dear father, come home.

Chance Newton quotes the first verse of this ballad in his account of G.H. Chirgwin. Chirgwin's early successes were not on the halls but as a child, persuading his father to come home from the public house. It formed, says Newton, "a kind of 'living picture'" (ironically commenting on the other kind of "tableau vivant") of the situation in the song, "Father, Dear Father." Nevertheless Chirgwin chose to follow a successful music-hall career by keeping a pub.

Unfortunately, even when such a father did come home, it could be an unmixed blessing:

> My father came home yester even,
> Reeled home thro' the mud and the rain;
> He upset the lamp on the table,
> And struck my sick mother again.

One can't help wondering, in a society that guards property more jealously than lives, whether to upset the lamp might not have been an even more heinous crime than striking a sick mother.

In isolation, such pathetic "renditions" nearly always sound absurd. In part this is because we are accustomed to expect these songs to make us laugh and it is most unusual to hear them sung well and with conviction. I am not going to argue that these songs have an artistic value usually denied them, but I would suggest that, "in their context in the music hall," expressed with deep sincerity, they made a crude but effective contrast, undercutting the belly-laugh context in which they appeared. This relationship is another indication of the capacity of popular dramatic audiences to make the swift transition from pathos to broad humour and back in the Robsonian manner noted in the commentary on "Villikins," and mentioned also in connection with Gracie Fields. What is also apparent is that the "message" of the temperance songs did not have much effect. Ironically, perhaps, the more one drank, the more one was moved to tears.

That such a song can be sincerely presented in a music hall suggests the existence of a tension that a consideration of the song in isolation, without external considerations being taken into account, fails to reveal. In the music hall there is a built-in impiety that undercuts excessive pathos. It is possible in such circumstances to play for a broader emotional response than is practicable in the legitimate theatre of the conventional kind. It is this illegitimate dramatic technique that O'Casey used in his early plays, and which Osborne in "The Entertainer," Pinter in "The Caretaker" and Beckett in "Waiting For Godot," have subtly exploited.

---

[1] In earlier verses it has chimed through one and two.

It is still possible to hear a pathetic song sung with complete conviction on old recordings. One that I have in mind, "Just Before The Battle, Mother," was a great favourite at genteel military nights presented by the Mohawk and similar minstrel groups. But, "on the page," it is hardly impressive and easily open to guying:

> Just before the battle, Mother,
> I am thinking most of you.
> While upon the field we're watching,
> With the enemy in view.
> Comrades brave are 'round me lying,
> Filled with thoughts of home and God;
> For well they know that on the morrow,
> Some will sleep beneath the sod.
> CHORUS:
> Farewell, Mother, you may never
> Press me to your breast again;
> But, Oh, you'll not forget me, Mother,
> If I'm numbered with the slain.

The bathos of "God" to "sod" and the pathetic picture of the grown son pressed to his fond mother's bosom, together with the vision of death, scarcely need pointing out. Yet this song, sung with intense force and conviction by Ernest Pike, a favourite singer of such ballads, on a record made some fifty years ago, demands a response out of all proportion to the words and music as they appear in cold print. From such a recording comes a hint of the kind of appeal songs of ripe surface emotion had when set in a context of cheerful, extroverted, broad comedy.

"Don't Go Out To-night, Dear Father" is my own favourite of all songs of this kind, if only because of that disastrous line: "Morning found the little pleader"— so invitingly suggesting precisely the wrong name for the little child. It requires an innocence that we have perhaps lost to be able to write or sing such a line sincerely and unambiguously. But there are other delights. There is first the pleasure which we now usually hasten to shrug off—the pleasure of open and unashamed emotion. Secondly there is a delight that springs from, it must be admitted, a sense of superiority most of us feel in the face of such songs—a perverse pleasure in their peculiar literary badness. For example, the drooping—bloom image: the idea that Papa might, through sheer stubborn drunkenness, miss the visit of the angels who are coming to take dear Mamma—as if it were the angels he ought to see, not his dying wife. And the unfortunate ambiguity in the second verse. Will father only say that he loves his wife to be lying in that cold, cold room? Again we know what is meant (and, to be fair, the comma after "Mamma" implies an informative rather than a definitive following phrase) but the ambiguity is not so easily shrugged off. It is a pity, too, that imagination ran dry at the end of the second verse so that the matter of the chorus had to be repeated again. Much the same sort of objections can be levelled against the music, with its painful pause on the penultimate note of the fifth bar of the chorus with, in the sixth bar, that falling minor seventh.

It is easy to score literary points against sentimental songs. They are open to parody (and the Victorians didn't hesitate to burlesque them) but one wonders sometimes whether our delight in parody does not in part hide our unease when confronted with emotion openly expressed. The loss we have sustained may be greater and more serious than the gain in aesthetic objectivity.

54

IN MY FUST 'USBANDS TIME

WRITTEN & COMPOSED BY

HARRY NICHOLLS,

SUNG WITH THE GREATEST SUCCESS BY

HERBERT CAMPBELL.

The Huntsman

Performed by Dan Leno for King Edward VII and Queen Alexandra.
Written by George A. Stevens and Albert Perry; Composed by Fred Eplett.
Copyright: Bowerman & Co.

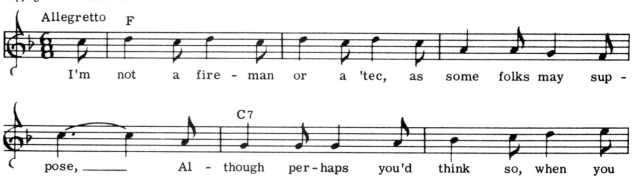

Allegretto   F

I'm   not   a   fire - man   or   a   'tec,   as   some   folks   may   sup -

C7

pose, ____   Al - though   per - haps   you'd   think   so,   when   you

I'm not a fireman or a 'tec, as some folks may suppose,
Although perhaps you'd think so, when you gaze upon my clothes.
At present I'm a huntsman gay, a huntsman gay am I,
And all the ladies smile at me, as through the air I fly.

PATTER:

Fly! Fly! Fly! Now, when you come to think of it, what
a harmless little creature the fly is. You see the other day I
was invited down to the Duchess of Piccadilly Circus's county
seat to attend the meet. Now when I say "attend the meet," I
don't wish you to mistake me for a pork butcher. No! I mean
hunting the hares. Now, by hunting the hares, I don't wish
you to mistake me for a hairdresser. To be explicit, hunting
the hares means following the hounds; and they were a lot of
hounds, especially Lord De No Oof, because just to show that
I was used to hunting, I shouted in his ear, "Tally Ho!" He
turned pale and nearly fainted. He thought I said "Tally-man."
But after all, following the hounds is a splendid life. The
bugles buge, the post-horns horn, and the horses horse.

Now, as soon as I received the invitation, I set about
getting a huntsman's costume, and you will observe that I
got it. Now I'll let you into a secret. This costume was
not made for me at all. It's all over me. This is a proper
huntsman's costume, because you have to hunt all through it
before you can find me. As I stated before, I took the train
by the London, Cheatem and Over [the London Chatham and Dover],
and as soon as I arrived at Toad-in-the-Hole there was the
barrow waiting for me—I beg pardon, I mean the Baron—and
when we arrived at the mansion there was an accident. I found
that my luggage was missing. Her ladyship remarked, "Perhaps
you have left it at the station." I said, "No! no! I don't
think so—(very deep in thought)—no, I could not have left
it at the station. Ah! I have it." Then I suddenly recollected
that I had placed it in my hat for safety—a piece of Sunlight
soap, and a packet of Tibbles.

Then the Baron said, "Now we will go to the meet." I
couldn't see any meat. I looked round, but only saw a lot
of empty plates; I think they must have eaten all the meat
for breakfast. Well, then they put me up in a beautiful set of
apartments—lovely furniture—ancient; I knew it was ancient
when I looked at it. Why, the sofa was hard up for a leg.
And the bed. Ah! the bed! Splendid! It was one of those
double, triple, springy, slip-away, stop-wherever-you-are, no
kind of bed at all. You know, sort of a cross-breed, between a
bed and a switchback railway. I never did see such a lovely
bit of architecture in my life. It was—well, I did not stop
to criticise everything in the room. My mind was so full of
hunting. I was dreaming of hunting all night.

Next morning we came down to breakfast as happy as hares.
And what a fine breakfast we had. So many different courses—
kippers and marmalade. We thoroughly enjoyed ourselves. Young
Lady Evelyn, the daughter—jolly young cat—flirting with me
all the time. She was squeezing my hand and so on, and she
kept on (just for fun) sticking bits of marmalade on my face.
When we finished, we donned our costumes and started off to
the meet—to the meet. The horn sounded and pip, pip, away
we went on our bicycles—I mean our chestnuts. When I say
chestnuts, I don't mean stale jokes. No. Horses, horse, not

elephants, horses. Away we dashed over the dillies and dallies, and I caught the hare. But I could never see the use of spending all this time and taking all this trouble in catching the hare. I have come to the conclusion that it is much easier to go into a poultry shop and buy one. At any rate, I caught it. I was riding along, breakneck pace, when I saw something darting past the hedge. Said I, "That's the hare," and taking deliberate aim, I exerted my strength and threw my gun at it. Then I shouted to my friends behind, "Tally Ho! Tally Ho! Tally Ho! I've got it." Then springing from my horse, I rushed towards the jungle—I beg pardon, I mean the hedge—and withdrew the animal. Then we gazed upon it. And the poor cat was dead.

CHORUS:
Away, away, away, away, away, away, away we go:
I don't know where we go, but still I know we go away.
Away, away, away, away, away, away, away we go:
I don't know where we go, but still I know we go away.
I've played at various hunting games since I've been on this earth,
But of that class of hunting I never knew the worth.
I won't infer that I have never hunted hares before,
Because at home, when we've had soup, I've found them by the score.

PATTER:
Well, I had never done any real hunting before. I am a tripe-dresser by persuasion. So the Baron told me when I came to the ditch to take it—I took it. Well, when I say took it, I suppose I took a pint and a half. I would not take another liqueur of ditch for anything. There was a kind of blancmange at the bottom, and a verdigris at the top. Then the Baron told me to follow the scent. I said, "You follow it, I have quite enough here to last me for a month!" But although I don't know much of hunting in the true sense of the word, I did very well for a beginner. First over the hedge every time— very often before the horse. You know, the horse is a very beautiful creature—so affectionate, so docile, so tame, I love it. Well, I am particularly in love with the horse I rode. I had not ridden a hundred yards when my affection so overcame me that I clasped my arms tightly round his neck and would not let go.

Gone away! What do they say that for? There is no necessity. We know the hares have gone away. In fact, to my idea they would be very silly to linger about on such occasions. It stands to reason. Do you mean to tell me that if you were a hare that you would be waiting about for me to come up with a gun, loaded with old nails, bits of paper, and scraps of boot-leather? No! You would have an important appointment somewhere else. Why, I'd sooner have one little game of hunt the slipper than forty hunt the hares.

Chorus

Dan Leno, as was confessed on his behalf, "came into the world a mere child" but became a farthing millionaire with "an acre and two pints of some of the best wasp-stalking in the kingdom." This way of introducing Leno in *Hys Booke* was typical of his act and himself.[1] Although he performed in London for less than 20 years, Leno became a legend before his early death in October, 1904. One of the many much moved by his loss was Max Beerbohm, who attempted to evaluate his genius. Unlike Albert Chevalier, wrote Beerbohm, Leno was no inaugurator; at most "he shifted the centre of gravity from song to patter." His theme was ever "the sordidness of the lower middle class, seen from within. Yet, in his hand, how gloriously it blazed, illuminating and warming! All that trite and unlovely material, how new and beautiful it became for us through Dan Leno's genius!" It was, considered Beerbohm, Leno's personality that made his act what it was universally claimed to be, for he was "a creature apart, radiating an ethereal essence all his own."

Beerbohm was not a man who by instinct was drawn to the music halls. Six years earlier, in 1898, he wrote, also in *The Saturday Review* (shortly after replacing George Bernard Shaw as its theater critic):

> The mass of people, when it seeks pleasure, does not want to
> be elevated: it wants to laugh at something beneath its own
> level. Just as I used to go to Music Halls that I might feel my
> superiority to the audience, so does the audience go that it
> might compare itself favourably with the debased rapscallions
> of the songs.

If Beerbohm's tribute of Leno is in a very different vein, it was perhaps because it was Leno in particular who enabled him to find a delight in the music hall less superior in its attitude than that revealed in this earlier essay.[2]

Without his personality to go with them, Leno's songs and acts, even more than those of other artists, are clearly but a shadow of what he made them. As he died in 1904, his recordings were made when techniques were very crude, so that although it is possible to hear his voice and gauge in some little way his approach, these recordings cannot do him even such justice as the restrictions of that medium would permit. Even without his personality to give it the inimitability of which every single writer who mentions him speaks of with a mixture of wonder and reverence, I have known a crude amateur performance of his monologue, "The Robin", to give considerable delight.

Yet, even without such a vital element of his act, the words that Leno sang and spoke may sometimes have considerable interest. "The Huntsman" is far more act than it is song, and the song indeed is virtually no more than a hunting cry. The patter is largely, but not entirely, absurd humour based on the association of ideas, and it makes possible the kind of scene painting in words in which Leno specialised.

---

[1]*Dan Leno, Hys Booke* was presented by BBC on television in January, 1968 by the comedian Roy Hudd. It was revealed to everyone's surprise, when the programme was repeated some weeks later, that Leno had not himself written this book. The author proved to be T. C. Elder, now aged 99, who had earned his living as a professional ghost-writer.

---

[2]In his tribute to Leno, Beerbohm foresees the talking film: "Some day, no doubt, the phonograph and the bioscope will have been so adjusted to each other that we shall see and hear past actors and singers as well as though they were alive before us. I wish Dan Leno could have been thus immortalised. No actor of our times deserved immortality as well as he."

Taken in isolation, the humour is not very remarkable. For example, there is nothing excruciatingly comic about this:

> Then the Baron said, "Now we will go to the meet."
> I couldn't see any meat.
> I looked round, but only saw a lot of empty plates;
> I think they must have eaten all the meat for breakfast.

The rich humour of the whole act is not due to individually witty lines but to the accumulation of what, separately, are quite modest playings with words. The comic effect is partly achieved by skillful timing (working on the audience's anticipation and tricking expectancy), by variations in the types of play on words—puns, association of ideas, malapropisms, word formations—and by changes of tone. What is quite apparent is a delight in language and its possibilities which makes considerable demands upon an audience's capacity to listen intently and to bring imagination into play.

Even the brief extract just quoted shows Leno's capacity for building up a word picture and for creating an imaginative world. Furthermore his manner of imparting this information, his constant modification of one statement by another, his wistful surprise, the confidential tone, the sense that he is facing powers beyond his frail capacity, all impart to the simple humour, by association and the world of fantasy, an emotional richness which can dimly be sensed even in the old recordings.

Except in pantomime, in which he usually worked with the huge Herbert Campbell, Leno worked alone, a small figure, on a large bare stage, using fairly simple props. All was concentrated on the relationship between performer and audience.

Leno made considerable use of changes in tone. The interpolated comment on Lady Evelyn—"jolly young cat"—will get a laugh because of the violent change of tone. The remark is crude, there is no wit here; but the manipulation of tone is skillful and, in its less violent fluctuations, can be subtle. The technique is exactly that still used—and with great success—before popular and sophisticated audiences by the English comedian, Frankie Howerd. Slightly greater variation can be seen in this short passage, where slapstick, rather less violent humour, and then the humour of surprise, follow each other rapidly:

> Then springing from my horse, I rushed towards the jungle—
> I beg pardon, I mean the hedge—and withdrew the animal.
> Then we gazed upon it. And the poor cat was dead.

I am reminded here of the near-fatal sickness which afflicted the dog that so tormented Jerry in Albee's *The Zoo Story*. This looks at first sight simple stuff indeed, but the shifts in style and point of view, and the delightful conceit (dare I use such a word?) of withdrawing an animal from a hedge, together with the sense of Leno's not *quite* being in control of the events he is so anxious to dominate, make possible a much more richly comic effect than the words taken in isolation might suggest.

Although I have not paid much attention to reminiscence in these commentaries, I cannot forbear adding a brief anecdote about Leno in connexion with this song—and one which has not, I believe, appeared in print before.

A very old friend, Mrs. Helen Tresahar (who acted under the name of Daisy

Thimm) travelled to Sandringham in the same train as did Leno. She had a small part in the sketch *Scrooge*, which was being presented by Sir Seymour Hicks in the same program before King Edward VII as that in which Leno was performing "The Huntsman." Leno, though the idol of the halls, suffered agonies of nervousness especially in the course of working up his acts. The importance of this occasion so worried him that throughout the journey he was sick time and again.

Dan Leno

At My Time of Life

Sung by Herbert Campbell. Words and Music by T. W. Connor.
Copyright: Francis, Day & Hunter, Ltd.

Allegretto

Now ev - er since I tied the knot, and which it ain't a

day, I've sat - is - fied my hus - band in my good old - fash - ioned

way. But since he's seen a gal in "bags", it's knocked him sure as

fate. He says I ain't worth that, be - cause I am not up to

date. ___ Chorus: There was none o' yer "High - ty Fligh - ty" girls, yer

"Hi - Tidd - ley Hi - ty" girls, When my old "Stick - in - the - mud"

took me for a wife. Now fan - cy me a-

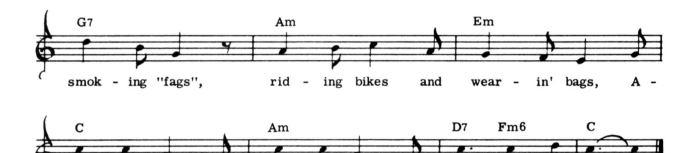

smok - ing "fags", rid - ing bikes and wear - in' bags, A -
leav - ing off my bits o' rags, At *my* time o' life! ____

Now ever since I tied the knot, and which it ain't a day,
I've satisfied my husband in my good old-fashioned way.
But since he's seen a gal in "bags," it's knocked him, sure as fate.
He says I ain't worth that, because I am *not* up to date.

CHORUS:
There was none o' yer "Highty Flighty" girls, yer "Hi-Tiddley Hity" girls,
When my old "Stick-in-the-mud" took me for a wife.
Now fancy me a-smoking "fags," riding bikes and wearin' bags,
A-leaving off my bits o' rags at *my* time o' life!

I like my drop o' "stimulant" as *all* good ladies do,
A 'arf a quartern, "two out," used to do between the two;
But now he says it's only "roughs" as patronizes "pubs",
For all "new Women" wot *is* "class" belongs to swagger clubs!

CHORUS:
There was none o' yer "Highty Flighty" girls, yer "Hi-Tiddley Hity" girls,
When my old "Thing-a-my-bob" took me for a wife.
Now fancy me old "Mother Scrubs" a-jine-ing these "ere Totties" clubs.
Fancy me deserting "pubs" at *my* time o' life!

He'd like to see me got up with a cigarette to puff;
A "dickey dirt" and tie (as if I wasn't guy enough!)
Says I'd look well in "bloomers" and a "call-me-Charlie" hat!
If *I'd* proposed it he'd 'a said, "Get out, yer gay old cat!"

CHORUS:
There was none o' yer "Highty Flighty" girls, yer "Hi-Tiddley Hity" girls,
When my old "Fourpenny-bit" took me for a wife.
Now fancy me a sportin' shirts! Playing billiards, backing "certs"
A-goin' about without my skirts at *my* time o' life!

Two of the conventions of pantomime are that the leading male part shall be played by a young and shapely female and that a place should be found for a dame, usually of generous proportions, who shall be played by a male comedian. "At My Time Of Life" is a "dame" song, and it was sung by one of the members of what has become a legendary pantomime team: Herbert Campbell and Dan Leno. Campbell played in the Drury Lane pantomime for 22 years and for the last 14 was partnered by Leno. The run but in a sense not the partnership was only broken by death. Campbell, who was born in 1844, died in July, 1904; Leno died three months later.

The dame tradition is a curious one and, although it was long accepted as no more than innocent dressing up in an age when convention was much stricter than it is now, there lurks beneath it a suggestion of something perverse. Occasionally a performance, even in this day and age, will be such that it brings down the wrath of critics because of the freedom of its sexual play in a show designed primarily for children. Thus quite often there is in such performances, for all their supposed innocence, an underlying tension. Barbette's act took this change of sex to its furthest extreme in the popular theatre in a low-wire act of 1923. After a strip act, Barbette performed on a low wire and, at the completion of the act, jumped down to the stage, ripping off a wig to reveal the bald head of Mr. van der Clyde.

Herbert Campbell's performances seem, from contemporary reports, to have presented a boisterous, even stentorian, non-feminine character. Christopher Pulling quotes Gilbert Frankau as saying in his autobiography in 1939:

> In the so-called "naughty nineties," if Herbert Campbell
> or Dan Leno had put on high voices and waggled their
> hips, the audience would not even have known what they
> intended to convey. Knowing it, they would have hissed
> them off the stage.

Certainly this song, as roared out by the nineteen-stone Campbell, has only one innuendo. Nevertheless, in view of the songs about the aesthetic movement (such as Macdermott's "Hildebrandt Montrose"), one rather wonders whether audiences were *quite* as naive as Gilbert Frankau suggests.

"At My Time Of Life" is very much a topical song, as the words it picks out suggest. Many of them date (according to the *Oxford English Dictionary*) from the 1880s and 1890s, though some go back a little earlier: "bags" for "trousers" dates from 1860, "fags" from 1888, "certs" from 1889, and "bloomers" from 1896, although "bicycles" appeared in 1869 (though not women riding them) and "pubs" dates from four years earlier—the word, not the institution. Rather appropriately, the terms of endearment go back much further—"stick-in-the-mud" to 1733 and "thing-a-my-bob" to 1751. The object of scorn is, of course, the New Woman; and quite clearly in this song, a distinction is drawn between the classes. The "swagger clubs" were, presumably, those such as the Alexandria (1883), the first women's club of this period reserved exclusively for women, and the University Women's Club (1887). It is ironical that a song which treats of women trespassing on men's preserves should be sung by a man dressed as a woman! Note how attention is drawn to this in "as if I wasn't guy enough."

Apart from its use of current colloquialisms and its arch emphasis of particular expressions, the words lack vivid individuality. Only occasionally, as in the last line of verse three, is there an expression of any distinction. Nevertheless the song gives a little insight into what was considered acceptable at the time, and it has that attractive quality of self-deflation that is to be found in many music-hall songs. Rather unusually, the chorus is in a different time from that of the verses.

Campbell was famous in his own day for his ridicule of what seemed to him to be taken too seriously. We tend to have a straight-laced picture of straight-laced Victorians, but just as they had a notoriously reverse side to their outwardly rigid morality, so the sentimental and patriotic songs had their sentiments turned on their heads. Furthermore, in the music hall, the two forms existed side by side. Perhaps the most surprising example of all, in view of the generally held beliefs about Victorian loyalty to the monarch, is the song concerned with limiting the population, "Do It No More." Here is one verse from the Folkways Record by Derek Lamb:

> As the Queen and Prince Albert
> So buxom and pert,
> Were gaily conversing together one day,
> John Bull heard 'em talking
> As they were awalking,
> And V unto A so boldly did say:
> "The state is bewildering about little children
> And we are increasing,
> You know we have four.
> We kindly do treat 'em
> And seldom do beat 'em,
> So Albert, dear Albert,
> We'll do it no more.
> Do it no more,
> Do it no more,
> Albert, dear Albert, we'll do it no more."

Cambell's most famous parody is that of the patriotic song, "By Jingo," written by G. W. Hunt at the time of the Russo-Turkish War in 1878. The song was sung by the Great Macdermott, and it had enormous popularity. It was responsible for introducing the word "jingoism" into the English language (though "by jingo" a piece of conjurer's gibberish, goes back two hundred years before Hunt's song). The chorus went:

> We don't want to fight, but by Jingo if we do,
> We've got the ships, we've got the men,
> And got the money too.
> We've fought the Bear before, and while we're Britons true,
> The Russians shall not have Constantinople.

Patriotic songs are no easier to take than are the sentimental long after their day, but this chorus is worth quoting if only because it provides a perspective for Herbert Campbell's parody:

> I don't want to fight, I'll be slaughtered if I do;
> I'll change my togs, I'll sell my kit, and pop my rifle too;
> I don't like the war, I ain't a "Briton true,"
> And I'll let the Russians have Constantinople.

"I ain't a 'Briton true'" in mid-Victorian days!

Wilkie Bard, who is credited with introducing the "interrupted act" to the

Victorian halls, had a remarkable parody among a number of "rejection" songs:

> But when the bugle calls
> We shall march away as we did in days gone by.
> We shall march, march, march,
> Yes we'll march, march, march,
> April, May, June and July,
> When the bugle blows we shall march to war,
> And there's not a man will hear it.
> I don't care how soon the bugle calls,
> So long as I don't hear it.

Even Leslie Stuart's "Soldiers of the Queen" had cynical words put to it by Hayden Coffin at Daly's in 1895, though the original song did survive to become popular in the Boer War. The anti-Ibsen critic, Clement Scott, was one of those who took up Hunt's use of "by Jingo." In August, 1878, he wrote a song for a patriotic extravaganza called *Albion's Nationality* at the Oxford Music Hall in a bill which featured George Chirgwin, Arthur Roberts, and Jenny Hill, the Vital Spark. The second verse of Scott's song runs:

> We have suffered in silence the impudent banter,
> Of Cowards that swore that foul war was our cry,
> Come pledge our false friends in a merry decanter,
> They shot behind hedges—we never said die!
> We can laugh—we have won—though they dragged the old island
> To a verge of a precipice loyalty shuns.
> But in spite of deserters—on ocean and dry land,
> By Jingo! old England has stood to her guns.

The ambiguities alone make this astonishing, never mind its tone. In the same programme, G. W. Hunt had written the words and music for "Japanorevelrie," with "Positions and Attitudinisations" by Mr. Paul Valentine of the Theatre Royal, Covent Garden. The range of contrast is remarkable.

Herbert Campbell was also fond of ridiculing sentimentality, as in his version of "Shall I Be An Angel, Daddy," which George Robey quotes in *Looking Back on Life*:

> You'll never be an angel, Daddy,
> With wings up in the sky;
> You'll never be an angel, Daddy,
> Along with Ma and I!
> You'd better look to your p's and q's
> Before you come to die—
> But you'll never be an angel, Daddy,
> And so you needn't try!

This is hardly witty and in this it differs little from most parodies of this kind sung on the halls. Possibly for this reason, less attention has been given to them than they deserve, but they are important for two reasons. First of all they indicate a greater complexity in social attitudes than is sometimes suggested; and, because these guying versions were able to exist alongside sincerely expressed patriotic and sentimental ballads, they are evidence of the paradoxical nature of the response of which the popular audience was then—and probably is still now—capable.

The Swimming Master

Sung by Dan Leno. Written and Composed by Herbert Darnley.
Copyright: Bowerman & Co.

When the wa-ter is wet and the air is dry A beau-ti-ful sight you may then es-py, On the pier in the sum-mer-time there am I Teach-ing the la-dies to swim ____ Though fright-ened at first of the wa-ter they be, Their con-fi-dence soon will re-turn, don't you see, When they have feast-ed their eyes up-on me, And no-ticed my fig-ure so trim ____

Chorus:

As I teach the girls to float ____ the sea goes down each throat. ____ They say, "Oh Dear! I'm going to sink," I have them up with a charm-ing wink. To my

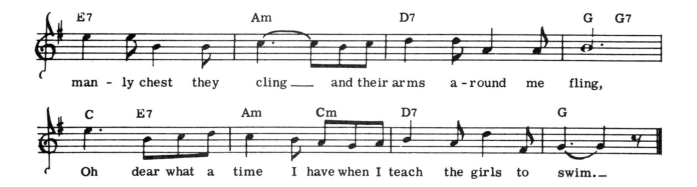

man - ly chest they cling ___ and their arms a - round me fling,

Oh dear what a time I have when I teach the girls to swim. ___

When the water is wet and the air is dry
A beautiful sight you may then espy,
On the pier in the summer-time there am I
    Teaching the ladies to swim.
Though frightened at first of the water they be,
Their confidence soon will return, don't you see,
When they have feasted their eyes upon me,
    And noticed my figure so trim

PATTER:
You didn't notice my figure when I first appeared—I came on
you too suddenly. You weren't able to grasp me altogether, as
it were—I'll go off and come on again. *(Retires off and
re-enters)* There! Now you can notice me properly. You see
you've got a north-east view of me. It is really remarkable
the effect I leave on people who see me for the first time.
When I walked on the pier last Monday, two ladies looked at
me and fell over into the water. I nearly got the Victoria
Cross for that. Of course, that was my chance. The moment
I saw the ladies in the water, quick as thought, I made one
dash to where they tied the boat up; untied the boat, got in,
and pulled out. But I was just too late. The ladies could
swim and they were saved. But it was a marvellous escape. If
I'd saved them I'd have got the medal. I've nearly got twenty
medals that way. I remember on another day something happened,
just the same—only of course different. I nearly got another
Victoria Medal. There was an old man, a very old man, all
bearded and wrinkled, lying asleep on the sand. I was up on
top, on the pr-pro-prom, on the pier. I dashed down before
anybody could stop me, siezed the old man, grabbed him by
the legs, up on to the gravel and on to the pavement. Saved
his life. There's not the slightest doubt if he had stayed
there asleep till the tide come up, he'd have been drowned.

CHORUS:
As I teach the girls to float, the sea goes down each throat.
They say, "Oh Dear! I'm going to sink,"
I have them up with a charming wink.
To my manly chest they cling and their arms around me fling,
Oh dear what a time I have when I teach the girls to swim.

My position is one of a deal of trust,
I'm so full of secrets I feel I could bust,
For the way some girls make up's enough to disgust—
    Still not a soul I've told
You would be surprised if some girls you could see,
Whose figures you think are from blemish quite free,
Why, do you know—that is—well, between you and me—
    Oh! I could a tale unfold.

PATTER:
I could tell you things you'd hardly believe—in
fact, I could tell you things I don't believe myself. There
was a strange lady came to me the other day and said, "Do you
mind my swimming with my stockings on?" I said, "No." Well,
out she ran, dived in, and came up feet first—there she was
bobbing up and down—I didn't know she'd got a cork leg.
Another lady asked me what I'd charge to teach her to swim.
I said, "One Guinea." She said, "Alright, I shan't be long,"
and went into the dressing room, a fine strapping figure. When
she came out, I didn't know her. I said, "I'll only charge
you half a guinea, 'cos there's only half of you to teach."

Chorus

Both the single and married I teach to dive;
The single young girls can sometimes contrive
To swim under water while I'm counting five;
    That's quite a record I call.
But Oh! I've tried, but I've found it in vain,
For diving the sweet married ladies to train.
They under the water can never remain,
They can't keep their mouths shut at all.

PATTER:
You wouldn't believe how strong you get having
so much to do with water. Before I taught swimming I was a
poor, weak little chap, with no chest and thin arms. Well,
now look at me! Oh, I love the water; all our family love
water—I've seen my father drink quarts of water—of course,
with something in it. And my brother, he's
passionately fond of water—he's a milkman. *(Turning as though
to someone who has just entered)* "Good morning, Miss Winkle,
good morning! Beautiful day indeed. Yes'm, ready if you are.
Well I never! What a pretty bathing dress! Made it yourself!
Ah! Don't you think you might have made a little more of it
while you were at it? It won't shrink! Well, I hope not.
Now then, ready—one, two, three,go! You dived rather
lumpy. That's right—don't struggle—keep cool. Don't talk,
you mustn't drink the water. Take nice quiet strokes—one,
two, three, my dinner's at four, five, six. Keep your head
up—head up! No! Keep that under. There! I knew that
dress wouldn't last—here's a pin."

Chorus

The patter to Dan Leno's song, "The Swimming Master," contains two styles closely associated with him. The opening is superb, yet it is difficult to pin down what it is that gives it its character. What is said is utterly simple and direct. There are no tricks and the only device in the opening lines is the suggestion that we have taken a north-easterly view of the man—quite the most attractive prospect, we should all agree. The contrast between a violent entry, a hurling across the stage—even when repeated, as indicated by the patter—does not completely account for the effect. The charm and the delight of these simple lines spring, I believe, from the creation of a sense of wonder and amazement at the plain and obvious.

Leno had, more than any other comedian I have heard in recordings or in life, the capacity for extracting wonderment and surprise out of the obvious. It is perhaps this remarkable capacity which accounts for the amazing unanimity amongst all who speak of him. Were he dependent largely upon device, physical or verbal, it would not appeal to some, or it would pall; but the ability—the creative power—to evoke wonderment at the ordinary—by a simple stance, a non-existent robin, an egg—is exhilarating and of universal appeal.

Leno, of course, had his devices. Playing with language has already been mentioned, and in "Young Men Taken In and Done For," there is the comic presentation of the pathetic or defeated which is not uncommon in popular tradition. "The Swimming Master," like "The Huntsman," reveals Leno's capacity to word-paint; it also shows humour derived from incongruity (in the comparison of what he was and what he is now—still a tiny figure) and from extension or modification (the quarts of water with something in them), but it is at the end of the patter that there is to be found one of his most successful techniques: peopling the stage with characters.

Max Beerbohm remarks in his essay that Leno did not attempt vocal imitations of the characters he created. As in the patter printed here, his own responses give the gist of what has been said to him. The dialogue and the characterisation seem complete, yet Leno has not had to step out of himself. Thus he is able to direct his audience's apprehension entirely through himself, so as to never break or modify the intimate link built up between himself and his audience.

I should like to take one further point from Max Beerbohm's tribute to Dan Leno's technique, partly because it reveals an aspect of Leno's technique, but also because it suggests how important the audience is in the creation of the whole performance in popular drama:

> A new performance by Dan Leno was almost always a dull
> thing in itself. He was unable to do himself justice
> until he had, as it were, collaborated for many nights
> with the public. He selected and rejected according to
> how his jokes, and his expression of them "went"; and
> his best things came to him always in the course of an
> actual performance, to be incorporated in all the
> subsequent performances...
>
> The technique for acting in a music-hall is of a harder,
> perhaps finer, kind than is needed for acting in a
> theatre; inasmuch as the artist must make his effects
> so much more quickly, and without the aid of any
> but the slightest "properties" and scenery and without
> the aid of any one else on the stage.

The role of the audience can be examined in a recording of a monologue on a similar subject made by Max Miller (who lurks behind Archie Rice in John Osborne's *The Entertainer*). The act was recorded live at a wartime concert for factory workers—that is, about 25 years ago and some 40 years after Leno made his recording. The innuendo is broad, though as Miller would say, it's all in our own minds, and the reaction of the audience makes it possible for us to gauge something of that remarkable interaction of performer and audience which is perhaps the most significant feature of music hall. It is this interplay that we have to imagine for Leno, and which, I believe, was also significant in Elizabe-

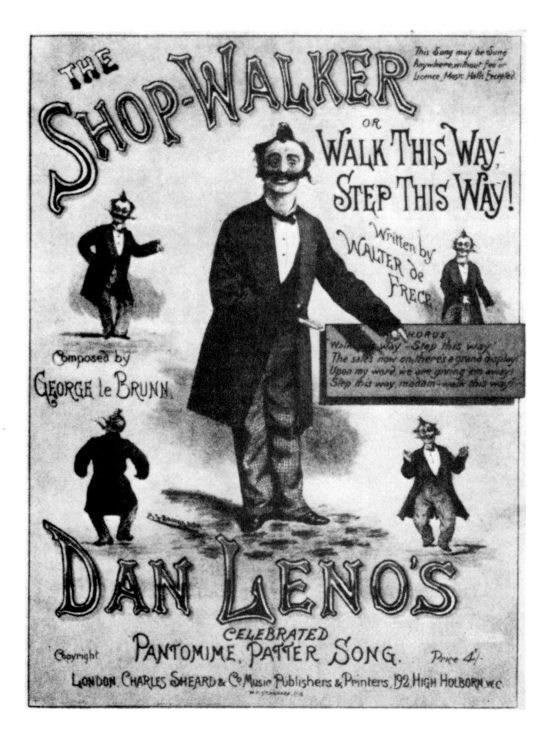

than and Jacobean theater. In this extract from Miller's act I have indicated audience laughter by the letter 'L' in brackets. Miller is teaching a young lady to swim—three miles out at sea: 'I don't mess about on the shore.'

Then she said, 'Now I think I'll turn over' (L). And as she turned over, may the sand get in my eyes if I tell a lie (L), as she turned over, I slipped my hand underneath to hold her up—otherwise she'd go down (L). I'm entitled to do that because I'm the swimming instructor, y'see (L). I got my hand underneath: she's lying on her back, on the top of the water—her head'll be about there, her feet there, and my hand'll be about (slight pause) (L) Nah! Shut up! No! Shut up! (*Over increasing laughter*) No. Well, I've lost me place now (L). Listen. Listen, listen (*very rapid*) all of a sudden, all of a sudden, she gave a scream—not a very loud scream—she went (*sexual moan*) (L) (*He chuckles*) (L) Twice. I didn't hear her the first time—I was creeping up on her (L). I said, 'What are y'screaming for?' She said, 'A shrimp's bitten me' (L). I said, 'Don't be a mug, it's me.' I said, 'You want confidence.' She said, 'You want hand-cuffs' now listen (L) listen (L)....

Notice Miller's technique in building up laughs and, when he breaks the continuity of the dramatic illusion by saying he has lost his place in the script, how he wins a laugh for that and then by speaking rapidly and repetitively he gets the audience involved again in the situation he is describing. The ability to sketch a scene in words clearly and rapidly is also worth noting.

It was the audience more than the stars, the words, or the music, and its intimate relation with the performer that gave the English music hall its vigour and characteristic power in its hey-day. It is this relationship that is so difficult to recapture for it springs—as one imagines it did in the late Tudor period—more from social conditions and the conjunction of many circumstances than from what is still left to us—words and music on paper or disc.

In the circumstances it seems foolhardy even to attempt to suggest the nature of a performance given by Leno from the evidence of words and music alone, for so much of the artist is inevitably lacking. Furthermore the printed versions of Leno's songs and patter are not necessarily those that he finally developed. The patter after the first verse of "The Swimming Master" can be compared with a recording Leno made, and the latter (which I have used where appropriate) is superior to the printed text.

Without producing parallel texts, which these circumstances hardly warrant, it is not possible to discuss these changes fully, but two small examples may be of interest. The patter printed here refers to the Victoria Cross and later to the Victoria Medal. The printed source has "the Humane Society Medal." The latter is a genuine, real-life possibility. The Victoria Cross is awarded only for gallantry in the face of an enemy in armed conflict, and there is no Victoria Medal. In other words the fantasy is a little further removed from reality and the comic point heightened.

In the first verse of the song, the printed source has, "Their confidence soon will return you will see," whereas Leno sang, "don't yer see." Such a slight change may be fortuitous or merely a lapse, but the sung version suggests a refining of the act, even in such a casual detail, along the lines Max Beerbohm describes. It is not that the words are themselves vitally different but that the intonation is, in this way, subtly shifted.

Young Men Taken In And Done For

Sung by Dan Leno. Words and Music by Harry King.
Copyright: Francis, Day & Hunter, Ltd.

Moderato

D / A7

As smart a man as ev - er lived was I when in my

D / G / A7

prime, Un - til I met Miss Lu - cy Jaggs, she knocked me out of

D / A / F♯m / B7 / E7

time. I called there for a - part - ments for I'd no - ticed once or

A / B7 / E / E7 / A

twice, A card stuck in the win - dow, and on it this de - vice:

Chorus: Tempo di Marcia

D / A7 / D / G / F♯7 / A7

"Young men tak - en in and done for," Oh! I nev - er thought that she, The

Bm / Em6 / Ddim / D / D♯dim / Em / A7 / D

girl I left my hap - py home for, Would have tak - en in and done for me.

74

Dan Leno

As smart a man as ever lived was I when in my prime,
Until I met Miss Lucy Jaggs, she knocked me out of time.
I called there for apartments, for I'd noticed once or twice,
A card stuck in the window, and on it this device:

CHORUS:
"Young men taken in and done for,"
Oh! I never thought that she,
The girl I left my happy home for,
Would have taken in and done for me.

Being a lonely single man, I wanted lodgings bad,
So Lucy Jaggs's mother then soon showed me what she had.
I'd not stayed there above a week when Lucy came to me
And fondly kissed me on my cheek, then sat me on her knee.

Of course, just like a stupid, I must go and tie the knot
That brings us bliss and happiness—but that's all tommy rot.
I don't believe my wife loves me, it's the truth I'm telling you.
A wife can't love her husband much if she beats him black and blue.

Although sentimental ballads of the most lachrymose kind were popular in the music halls, as often as not marriage itself was treated in matter-of-fact terms or else ironically. "The Future Mrs. 'Awkins" is unusual in that, though it is down-to-earth, it is also tender without becoming unduly sentimental. "We All Go To Work But Father" and "Young Men Taken In and Done For," on the other hand, offer a view of married life that might comfort the singers of "Waiting at the Church" and "Cushie Butterfield" and dispel the exuberance of the prospective bride of "Half-past Nine."

About this time there was a number of songs which referred to men in lodgings. Vesta Victoria had a lodger who was such a nice young man, and Alf Chester plaintively asked why he had left his little back room for marriage:

> What a mug I must have been
> I might as well be dead and buried,
> Oh! God save our gracious Queen.

"Young Men Taken In and Done For" presents an ironic picture of deception and disillusionment. In its modest way it is drawn, in Max Beerbohm's words, from within the world that Dan Leno knew so well, but it is not taken quite far enough. The chorus follows each verse effectively, becoming at its last appearance, almost bitter; for despite the comic exaggeration of the last line of the song, the flat "I don't believe my wife loves me" suggests a feeling of emptiness surprising in a comic song and this is carried through into the final chorus. It is a pity that the anti-festive character of the third verse is not a little more strongly realised, for this would help turn what is no more than a run-of-the-mill music-hall song into something considerably more interesting. Nevertheless, in the hands of a competent artist, never mind a Dan Leno, an audience could be persuaded very easily to join in this chorus—the men at least.

I've Got Rings On My Fingers

Written by R. P. Weston and F. J. Barnes;
Composed by Maurice Scott. Sung by Ellaline Terriss.
Copyright: 1909, Francis, Day & Hunter, Ltd.

Now Jim O' Shea was cast a-way up-on an In-dian Isle. The na-tives there they liked his hair, They liked his I-rish smile, So made him chief Pan-jan-drum, The Na-bob of them all. They called him Jij-ji-boo Jhai, And rigged him out so gay, So he wrote to Dub-lin Bay, To his sweet-heart just to say:

Chorus: Sure, I've got rings on my fin-gers, bells on my toes, El-e-phants to ride up-on, my lit-tle I-rish

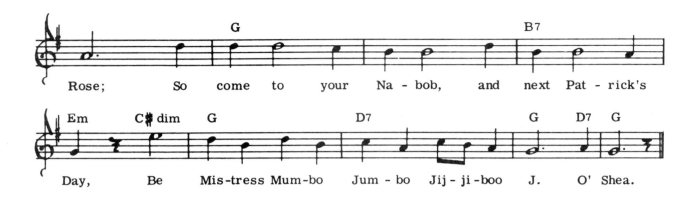

Rose; So come to your Na - bob, and next Pat - rick's

Day, Be Mis-tress Mum-bo Jum - bo Jij - ji -boo J. O' Shea.

Now Jim O'Shea was cast away
Upon an Indian Isle.
The natives there they liked his hair,
They liked his Irish smile,
So made him chief Panjandrum,
The Nabob of them all.
They called him Jij-ji-boo Jhai,
And rigged him out so gay,
So he wrote to Dublin Bay,
To his sweetheart, just to say:

CHORUS:
Sure, I've got rings on my fingers, bells
    on my toes,
Elephants to ride upon, my little
    Irish Rose;
So come to your Nabob, and next
    Patrick's Day,
Be Mistress Mumbo Jumbo Jij-ji-boo
    J. O'Shea.

Across the sea went Rose Magee
To see her Nabob grand.
He sat within his palanquin,
And when she kissed his hand,
He led her to his harem,
Where he had wives galore.
She started shedding a tear;
Said he, "Now have no fear,
I'm keeping these wives here
Just for ornament, my dear."

In emerald green he robed his queen,
To share with him his throne.
'Mid eastern charms and waving palms
They'd shamrocks, Irish grown,
Sent all the way from Dublin
To Nabob J. O'Shea.
But in his palace so fine,
Should Rose for Ireland pine,
With smiles her face will shine
When he murmurs, "Sweetheart mine":

78

It always comes as something of a surprise to find that it is not Ellaline Terriss who has the rings on her fingers, but one Jim O'Shea. "I've Got Rings on My Fingers" is as jolly a piece of nonsense as any, and it has an appropriate gaiety of tune to go with it. It is almost uncharitable to expect logic in such a song, but it is a little odd of Nabob J. O'Shea to keep state in his palanquin, however gaudily arrayed. And would Miss Magee have shed only a tear on being led to a harem to see wives galore? But this is hardly a song for questions of this kind. It stands on its own terms as engaging nonsense and nothing else.

The chorus of another of Ellaline Terriss's songs, "The Honeysuckle and the Bee," was included in an impromptu sing-song by the workmen in Robert Tressell's *The Ragged Trousered Philanthropists*. The "programme" in which it was featured makes interesting reading, for it reveals the kind of contrast to which reference is made in discussing "Don't Go Out Tonight, Dear Father" and "At My Time Of Life."

First came the "old favorite," "Work for the Night Is Coming." The chorus of this hymn was taken up by nearly everyone. Then "imitating the whine of a street-singer," one of the men started, "Oh Where Is My Wandering Boy To-night." This was followed by "a choice selection of choruses of well-known music-hall songs, including 'Goodbye, My Bluebell,' 'The Honeysuckle and the Bee,' 'I've Got 'Em,' and 'The Church Parade,' the whole being tastefully varied and interspersed with howls, shrieks, curses, catcalls, and downward explosions of flatulence." Tressell is not, of course, writing a novel about the music hall, but this description gives a good impression of one kind of rowdy tap-room entertainment of which the music hall proper was a not-too-distant relative.

Ellaline Terris often performed duos with her husband, Sir Seymour Hicks (one called *You and I* was included in the Command Performance at Sandringham in January 1904 when Leno performed *The Huntsman*). Her father, William Terriss, was a successful actor. He had the misfortune to be mistaken for William Abingdon, the stage villain of Adelphi dramas, and was stabbed to death by a madman on the way into the Adelphi on 16th December, 1897.

Are We To Part Like This, Bill?

KATE CARNEY.

Words and music by Harry Castling and Charles Collins.
Sung by Kate Carney.
Copyright: B. Feldman & Co., Ltd.

Three weeks a - go, no lon - ger, I was as

gay as a bird on the wing, But since me and

Bill have been part - ed, you know, Life is a blank and it's

changed ev' - ry - thing. I saw him out with an - oth - er that

night, None can guess how __ I felt at the sight, With __

tears in my eyes that I tried to keep back, I

crept to his side and said: ____ Are we to

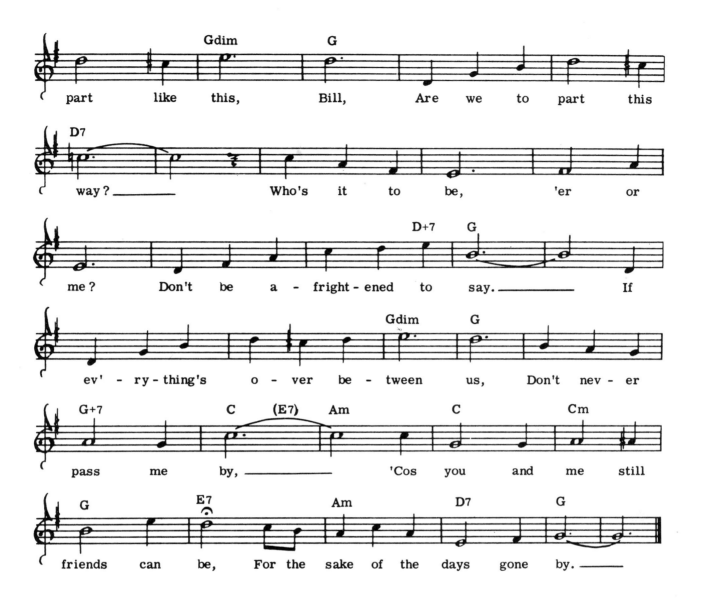

part like this, Bill, Are we to part this way? _____ Who's it to be, 'er or me? Don't be a-fright-ened to say. _____ If ev'-ry-thing's o-ver be-tween us, Don't nev-er pass me by, _____ 'Cos you and me still friends can be, For the sake of the days gone by. _____

Three weeks ago, no longer,
I was as gay as a bird on the wing,
But since me and Bill have been part-
   ed, you know,
Life is a blank and it's changed
   ev'rything.
I saw him out with another that night,
None can guess how I felt at the sight,
With tears in my eyes that I tried to
   keep back,
I crept to his side and said:

CHORUS:
Are we to part like this, Bill,
Are we to part this way?
Who's it to be, 'er or me?
Don't be a-frightened to say.
If everything's over between us,
Don't never pass me by,
'Cos you and me still friends can be,
For the sake of the days gone by.

We went to school together,
Lived side by side, me and Bill, in the
   mews.
When 'e was ill, too, I stayed up for
   nights,
Nursed him—to do it I'd never refuse;
'E used to tell me his wife I should be—
I never thought that he'd turn against
   me,
Sleeping or waking, at work or at home,
I find myself murmuring this:

Down in a little laundry,
Me and 'er work side by side every day;
She was my pal and I looked to 'er well,
Trusted and helped 'er in every way.
Still if my Bill cares for 'er more than
   me,
I wish 'em no harm—no, but prosperity;
I try to forget him, but each day I find
These words running through my mind:

The music hall had its full share of songs redolent with sentimentality, but from time to time, sentiment was expressed in songs such as "The 'Ouses In Between," where humour undercut the sentiment and provided a tension with it; or, more rarely, in songs where the hard facts of a very ordinary life were so interwoven with the sentiment that the sentiment seemed to spring out of the hard stone of experience, thus carrying a conviction that the solely sentimental never did. Chevalier sometimes succeeded in this (but not in "The Fallen Star"), and Kate Carney's "Are We To Part Like This, Bill?", despite some literary awkwardness, makes its pathos convincing and acceptable.

The melody is more interesting than are those of many music-hall songs, and it is particularly expressive of the words. Triteness is close in both at times, but even the D, C sharp, C natural that accompanies "part this way" in the chorus, does just about escape, managing, despite the effect of cliche, to express poignantly the singer's emotion. So too with the rising fourth on the last word of each verse.

The words are a curious mixture of flatness ("Life is a blank, and it's changed everything") and the expression of a selflessness that hovers between a genuinely felt magnanimity and comic self-martyrdom. This is apparent in the repetition of "Don't be frightened to say" and "Don't never pass me by," and even in the very gauche line, "I wish them no harm—no, but prosperity" (even worse in the original spelling: prosperetee!). The very awkwardness of these lines gives a sense of naturalness to the sentiment, as if these feelings were being painfully dragged out of actual experience. At the same time there is a tension between the two ways of looking at such selflessness that makes possible a certain tonal complexity.

It is Kate Carney's achievement that, like Bessie Bellwood in "Wotcher 'Ria," she seems to be able to give expression to a way of living she knows intimately. What also comes through strongly is the closeness of living together in the kind of life that is described. Bill and his former girl cannot help but meet, nor can she help but see him out with another girl. She has nursed him, they went to school together, and the two girls work side by side. It is more than a catalogue of relationships; it suggests the fabric of living in this particular kind of community. There is no escape from the past and the song makes clear the impingement of the past on the present. These references are exact but not forced, so that we feel very strongly the experience of life coming through what is, in many ways, an ordinary jilting, awkwardly told.

The situation revealed in the song suggests something further. Despite the assurances she says Bill gave her that she should be his wife, we cannot help but feel that she has assumed a deeper feeling in their relationship than even their constant association warranted. The arrival of another girl on the scene has rapidly revealed Bill's affection for her to be more shallow than either had assumed. It is a simple and common enough situation, but it is nonetheless hard to bear, and this the song adequately and quite subtly conveys.

"Are We To Part Like This, Bill?" may not be one of the world's greatest songs, but it does recreate with individuality, if variable skill, the experience and the emotions it evoked of a particular way of life.

✦ PROGRAMME. ✦

Monday, January 11th, 1904, & Every Evening.

Reduced Prices to Saturday Matinees

Fauteuils 3s.   *Other Seats 2s., 1s., and 6d.*

1 **Overture** ... "The Gladiators" ... *Fucik*
2 **Mr. Herbert Willison** ... Vocalist
3 **Miss Maggie Carr** Banjoist and Comedienne
4 **Mr. Tom Leamore** ... ... Comedian
5 **The Excelsior Quartette**
6 **The Bensons** ... ... Musical Comedians
7 **Mr. T. E. Dunville** ... .. Comedian
8 **Miss Ray Wallace** ... ... Mimic
9 **Collins & Hart** ... The Tramp Hunters
10 **Miss Vesta Victoria** ... Comedienne
11 **Mr. Gus Elen** Coster & Cockney Comedian
12 **Miss Blanche Ring** American Comedienne
13   **"THE FOLLIES"**
In a Selection from their Celebrated Pierrot Entertainment—
1 Opening Chorus   2 A Coup'e of Coons   3 Cat Quartette
4 Burlesque of (*a*) A French Mimodrame.
       (*b*) An English Musical Comedy.
       (*c*) A German Wagnerian Opera.
Written and Composed by H. G. PELISSIER.
Misses Marjorie Napier, Lucy Webling and Ethel Allandale.
Messrs. Norman A. Blumé, Dan Everard and H. G. Pelissier.

14 **Mr. Hamilton Hill** ... In a New Song,
           "GOOD LUCK, JAPAN"
15 **Miss Marie Lloyd**   Queen of Comediennes
16 **Selection** ... "Czardas" (No. 1) ... *Michiels*
17 **Mr. A. Bo Kon** ... Continental Juggler
18 **Mr. Joe O'Gorman** ... Irish Raconteur
19 **Mrs. Brown Potter** will recite her famous
Fiscal Poem, "THE PLEDGE OF A BRITISHER."
20 **Mr. Will Evans** In Sketch, "YACHTING"
21 **Sisters Dacre** ... Duettists and Dancers

Musical Director ... **MAURICE JACOBI**

The above Programme is subject to alteration, and the Management disclaim responsibility for the unavoidable absence of any Artiste announced to appear.
RONISCH Grand Piano used on stage supplied by Messrs. METZLER, 41 & 43, Great Marlboro' Street, W.

SPECIAL NOTICE.—To meet the requirements of the London County Council—The Public can leave the premises at the end of the performance by all exits and entrances; all doors, gangways and passages must be kept clear.

The fire-proof screen to the proscenium opening will be lowered at least once during every performance to ensure its being in proper working order.

MATINEE EVERY SATURDAY AT 2.15.

Manager ... ... PHILIP YORKE
Acting Manager ... ... JAMES HOWELL

And Her Golden Hair Was Hanging Down Her Back

Sung by Alice Leamar and Sir Seymour Hicks. By Felix
McGlennon. Copyright: Francis, Day & Hunter, Ltd., and
Trustees of the Felix McGlennon estate.

There was once a coun-try maid-en came to Lon-don for a trip, And her
gold - en hair was hang-ing down her back; ___ She was wea - ry of the coun-try so she
gave her folks the slip, And her gold-en hair was hang-ing down her back; ___ It was
once a vi - vid au-burn but her ri-vals called it red, So she
thought she could be hap-pier with an - o - ther shade in-stead. And she
stole the wash-ing so-da and ap - plied it to her head, And some
gold-en hair came stream-ing down her back. ___ But oh! Flo!

Chorus:

such a change you know, When she left the vil - lage she was

84

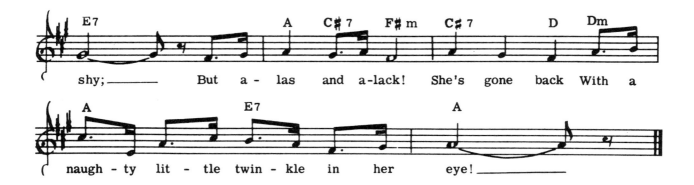

shy;⸺ But a-las and a-lack! She's gone back With a

naugh-ty lit-tle twin-kle in her eye!⸺⸺

There was once a country maiden came to London for a trip,
And her golden hair was hanging down her back;
She was weary of the country so she gave her folks the slip,
And her golden hair was hanging down her back;
It was once a vivid auburn but her rivals called it red,
So she thought she could be happier with another shade instead.
And she stole the washing soda and applied it to her head,
And some golden hair came streaming down her back.

CHORUS:
But oh! Flo! such a change you know,
When she left the village she was shy;
But alas and alack! she's gone back
With a naughty little twinkle in her eye!

She had a country accent and a captivating glance,
And her golden hair was hanging down her back;
She wore some little diamonds that came from sunny France
And her golden hair was hanging down her back;
She wandered out in London for a breath of ev'ning air,
And strayed into a Palace that was fine and large and fair—
It might be in a Circus or it might be in a Square,
But her golden hair was hanging down her back.

And London people were so nice to artless little Flo,
When her golden hair was hanging down her back;
That she had been persuaded to appear in a tableau
Where her golden hair was hanging down her back;
She posed beside a marble bath upon some marble stairs,
Just like a water nymph or an advertisement for Pears,
And if you ask me to describe the costume that she wears—
Well, her golden hair is hanging down her back.

She met a young philanthropist, a friend of Missus Chant,
And her golden hair was hanging down her back;
He lived in Peckham Rye with an extremely maiden aunt
Who had not a hair a-hanging down her back;
The lady looked upon him in her fascinating way,
And what the consequences were, I really cannot say,
But when his worthy maiden aunt remarked his coat next day,
Well, some golden hairs were hanging down the back.

One of the traditional ways of rousing laughter in illegitimate drama is by innuendo. The techique is not by any means new nor is it confined to illegitimate drama—it is to be found in Elizabethan plays of four hundred years ago. In the music hall, precisely what is assumed is left to the imagination of each member of the audience, but the implication is invariably of a kind delightfully described by Chance Newton as "cerulean," or "a touch of the blue bag." It was a favorite comic device of Max Miller's. By means of stressed rhymes he would lead an audience to expect a blue joke, but would so time what he said that he could rely on being interrupted by the loud laughter of the audience before he reached the significant word. He would then feel free to upbraid the audience vigorously for having dirty minds and giving him a bad name—and this technique was far from peculiar to Max Miller.

This device, like any other, can be badly done, or it can be carried through with the down-right cheek and superb sense of timing of a Max Miller. The performer's approach to the innuendo song varies. Slightly more teasing songs than "And Her Golden Hair" are "The Bird in Nellie's Hat" and "Mother's Advice," but they must be presented quite differently. The former must be sung knowingly, while the latter depends on childlike innocence of presentation.

"And Her Golden Hair" was originally sung by Alice Leamar, but it was taken up by Sir Seymour Hicks and sung for some six hundred nights in the musical, *The Shop Girl,* in 1894-5. Hicks was not a music-hall artiste but, from time to time, he performed on the halls with his wife, Ellaline Terriss, usually in sketches.

This song is one of the many that tells the story of the young innocent maiden who comes to the great city—and her golden hair was hanging down her back. Marie Lloyd had several such. Despite some padding, the song rises above the mundane for several reasons. It makes skillful use of the reiteration of the refrain, partly descriptive, partly an invitation to innuendo, but partly also a nice deflation of that very golden hair we are asked to admire—it was once a vivid auburn but her rivals called it red. There is also a neat variation in the refrain when it is used for the maiden aunt and there is a nice turn of phrase in calling her "extremely maiden."

To some extent the odd awkwardness is carried by the melody, which is particularly freely flowing with a successful onward movement that not only helps to keep the "story" moving but also assists in the integration of the refrain. The melody too has a very pleasant variation in rhythm. Much of the "story" is sung to quavers (common enough in such songs), but the refrain provides a contrast with its alternating dotted quavers and semi-quavers. The chorus takes the variation of rhythm further, for, in addition to the alternation of dotted quavers or semi-quavers with undotted notes, there are sustained notes for "Oh! Flo!" and, after the imitative music for "But alas and alack!", there are three stressed notes for "she's gone back" giving, as a whole, an ironic effect which neatly undercuts the formal expression of woe.

It ought to be explained perhaps that a popular advertisement for Pears soap in the late Victorian period showed a naked child; and that "Missus Chant" was Mrs. Ormiston Chant, who, in 1892, began a campaign described even by that violently anti-Ibsen drama critic, Clement Scott, as "Prudes on the Prowl." She also appears in Arthur Roberts's song, "In My 'Ansom."

The TIVOLI Programme

Reserved Fauteuils   5-0   Pit Stalls 2-0.   Pit   1-6
Orchestra Stalls   } 3-0   Upper Circle   1-0
Grand Circle   Boxes   from £1-11-6

POPULAR PRICE MATINEES EVERY SATURDAY AT 2.15 .

His Lordship Winked At The Counsel

Written by George Dance; Composed by Peter Conroy.
Sung by Harry Rickards. Copyright: Ascherberg, Hopwood & Crew, Ltd.

Allegretto

The Judge took his seat in the court-house one day, A nice Breach of Prom-ise to hear, ___ The Plain-tiff stepped up with a veil round her face, A love-ly and blush-ing young dear. ___ She looked at the Ju-ry a sly lov-ing glance, she smiled at the Coun-sel be-low, ___ Then turn-ing her soft pret-ty eyes to the Judge, She ten-der-ly mur-mured, "Hei ho!" ___

Chorus: His Lord-ship winked at the Coun-sel, The Coun-sel winked at the Clerk; ___ The Ju-ry passed a wink a-long And mur-mured, "Here's a lark!" ___ The Ush-er winked at the

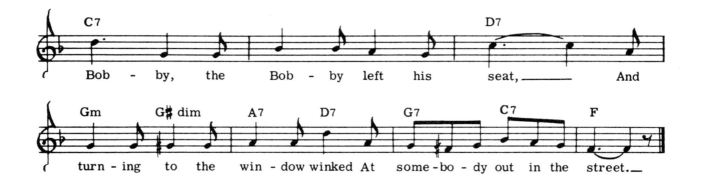

Bob - by, the Bob - by left his seat,_____ And
turn - ing to the win - dow winked At some-bo - dy out in the street._

The Judge took his seat in the court-house one
   day,
A nice Breach of Promise to hear,
The Plaintiff stepped up with a veil round her
   face,
A lovely and blushing young dear.
She looked at the Jury a sly loving glance,
She smiled at the council below,
Then turning her soft pretty eyes to the Judge,
She tenderly murmured, "Heigh-ho."

FIRST CHORUS:
   His Lordship winked at the Counsel,
   The counsel winked at the Clerk;
   The Jury passed a wink along
   And murmured, "Here's a lark!"
   The Usher winked at the Bobby,
   The Bobby left his seat,
   And turning to the window winked
   At somebody out in the street.

"Pray tell us the facts of your case," the Judge
   said,
"Your wrongs we are anxious to hear."
"I'll try, my good Lord," the sweet maiden
   replied,
"My poor heart is broken, I fear.
The monster who wooed me, declared on his
   oath,
He'd make me his bride by-and-by,
He took me long walks in the moonlight alone
And kissed me when no one was nigh."

SECOND CHORUS:
   His Lordship grinned at the Counsel,
   The counsel grinned at the Clerk;
   The Jury passed a grin along
   And murmured, "Here's a lark!"
   The Usher grinned at the Bobby,
   The Bobby left his seat,
   And turning to the window grinned
   At somebody out in the street.

The Judge took a pinch of his pungent rappee,
And dignity spread o'er his face.
"You really must name him, my sweet pretty
   maid,
Or we can't proceed with the case."
The maiden then snatched the thick veil from
   her cheeks,
And smiled like a mischievous elf;
Then turning around to the Judge cried, "My
   Lord,
That false-hearted man is yourself."

THIRD CHORUS:
   His Lordship blushed at the Counsel,
   The counsel blushed at the Clerk;
   The Jury passed a blush along
   And murmured, "Here's a lark!"
   The Usher blushed at the Bobby,
   The Bobby left his seat,
   And turning to the window blushed
   At somebody out in the street.

The Judge viewed the charms of the girl he once
   loved
And longed her lips once more to press
"Oh sweet pretty maid will you marry me now?"
She blushingly answered him, "Yes."
They sent for a Parson, they sent for a clerk,
And ere one short hour had sped,
They threw all the fusty law papers aside,
And each held a Prayer Book instead.

FOURTH CHORUS:
   His Lordship tickled the Counsel,
   The counsel tickled the Clerk;
   The Jury passed a tickle along
   And murmured, "Here's a lark!"
   The Usher tickled the Bobby,
   The Bobby left his seat,
   And turning to the window tickled
   At somebody out in the street.

There were literally dozens of music-hall songs about the police, and Christopher Pulling was able to devote a complete chapter to songs about policemen, but the life inside the Law Courts was not so well represented: perhaps they were beyond a joke. Certainly Charles Morton, the "Father of the Halls," had frequent battles with the law in order to win a measure of freedom for performances. Pulling does refer to one interesting legal song, "Would You Be Surprised to Hear?", which took its title from the introduction to many questions put to the Tichbourne claimant by the prosecuting counsel (but see the commentary to "I'm a Territorial"). Arthur Roberts had a very good act as a Queen's Counsel and Arthur Lloyd sang (as always, "with the greatest success") "I'll Place It in the Hands of My Solicitor." Nevertheless the attention paid to the law, apart from the police, was not as great as might have been expected.

The subject matter of this song is similar to that of Gilbert and Sullivan's *Trial by Jury* and the upshot is the same: judge and plaintiff marry. However, the music-hall song does not create the effect of surprise at the plaintiff's revelation that the judge's decision always manages to do in *Trial by Jury*, and the shift in tone between the third and fourth verses is awkwardly managed.

It is only rarely that language is precisely controlled in music-hall songs. The genre hardly encourages subtlety of this kind, but in this song, the language is particularly careless. A "nice" breach of promise?—yes, there is a suggestion here of the titillation of such an event and perhaps even a comment thereon. But "A lovely and blushing young dear" is too pat, too convenient without offering any particularity of description or modifying the tone. And why a *sly* loving glance for the Jury? Her slyness is more neatly put into practice in the last line of this verse.

The need to rhyme with "hear" in the second verse again makes for an insipid line. The third verse begins well with that rather remarkable consequence of taking "pungent rappee" (a coarse snuff), but it cannot manage without a particularly weak rhyme-word: "elf." But the game has been given away. Being able to re-create a sense of surprise, even when the song, act, or play, is known, is obviously not easy. Shaw can manage it, and Gilbert did in *Trial by Jury*, and, on the popular stage, it was evidently characteristic of Chirgwin. Here, doubtless because of the conventional-villain description of the judge at the opening of the third verse, we guess well in advance what will happen and the moment of "surprise" is kept hanging too long. The first two lines of the last verse have a careless lecherousness that is out of character in a frivolous song of this kind, and I don't think the song recovers from this.

Perhaps I have been a little harsh, too academically minded but, "His Lordship Winked at the Counsel" contrasts sharply with those music-hall songs which reveal insight or understanding, or possess individuality or unaffected gaiety. It is representative of a large number of songs that gained some popularity but are not in any way outstanding.

Harry Rickards, the singer of the song, did, as it happens, have unpleasant experiences in the law courts, for he was declared bankrupt. Of him Chance Newton makes one of his very rare adverse comments about the artistry of a performer (apart from his frequent complaints about "ceruleanism"). Rickards, he said, "was never really very artistic—that is, on the stage."

Where, presumably, his artistry did lie was in management, for he made a new start in Australia after his experience in the English law courts and became a most successful impresario. Florrie Forde was principal boy in his pantomimes before coming to England in 1897, and he managed Marie Lloyd and Alec Hurley on their successful visit to Australia in 1901.

By coincidence, the words of "His Lordship" were written by another music-hall personality who later became more famous as an impresario. George Dance wrote a number of music-hall songs, including some for Arthur Roberts, but he became noted for touring the George Edwardes musicals. He was knighted in 1923 in recognition of his gift of $85,000 to save the Old Vic from extinction.

Lily of Laguna

Sung by Eugene Stratton. Written and Composed by Leslie Stuart.

sun - down call - in' in de cat - tle up de moun - tain; I go 'kase she

wants me, ___ yes, 'kase she wants me help her do de call - in' and de count - in'.

She plays her mu - sic ___ to call de lone lambs ___ dat roam a -

bove, ___ But I'm de black sheep and I'm wait - in' For de

sig - nal of ma lit - tle la - dy love. She's ma la - dy love, she is ma

dove, ma ba - by love, She's no gal for sit - tin' down to dream,

She's de on - ly queen La - gu - na knows; I know she likes me, I know she

likes me be - kase she says so; She is de Lil - y of La -

gu - na, She is ma Lil - y and ma rose.

93

It's de same old tale of a palpatating nigger ev'ry time, ev'ry time;
It's de same old trouble of a coon
Dat wants to be married very soon;
It's de same old heart dat is longing for its lady ev'ry time, yes, ev'ry time,
But not de same gal, not de same gal.
She is ma Lily, ma Lily, ma Lily gal!
She goes ev'ry sundown, yes, ev'ry sundown
She goes ev'ry sundown, yes, ev'ry sundown callin' in de cattle up de mountain;
I go 'kase she wants me, yes, 'kase she wants me help her do de call-in' and de
    countin'.
She plays her music to call de lone lambs dat roam above,
But I'm de black sheep and I'm waitin'
For de signal of ma little lady love.

CHORUS:
She's ma lady love, she is ma dove, ma baby love,
She's no gal for sittin' down to dream,
She's de only queen Laguna knows;
I know she likes me,
I know she likes me,
Bekase she says so;
She is de Lily of Laguna, she is ma Lily and ma Rose.

When I first met Lil it was down in old Laguna at de dance, oder night;
So she says, "Say, a'm curious for to know
When ye leave here de way yer goin' to go,
'Kase a wants to see who de lady is dat claims ye all way home, way home
    to-night."
I says, "I've no gal, never had one."
And den ma Lily, ma Lily, ma Lily gal!
She says, "Kern't believe ye, a kern't believe ye, else I'd like to have ye
    shapperoon me;
Dad says he'll esscortch me, says he'll esscortch me,
But it's mighty easy for to lose him."
Since then each sundown I wander here and roam around
Until I know ma lady wants me,
Till I hear de music of de signal sound.

94

Perhaps the best pages of Macqueen-Pope's account of the music hall, *The Melodies Linger On*, are those in which he describes the work of Leslie Stuart and Eugene Stratton. Stuart, considers Macqueen-Pope, was "probably the greatest writer of songs the Music Hall ever had," and this partnership of one-time church organist and former minstrel performer was particularly fruitful. Macqueen-Pope describes with eloquence the kind of performance given by Stratton of Stuart's songs, the break-up of their partnership following a quarrel at a race meeting, and Leslie Stuart's dramatic comeback in 1928.

"Lily of Laguna" has been popular for three-quarters of a century, even without its greatest exponent to sing it and despite a greatly changed sensitivity to "coon" songs and to particular words—such as "nigger"—which Stuart used in an age when they did not rouse the opprobium they do now. Is this the popularity of nostalgia only? Was Stuart as great a composer as Macqueen-Pope thought him to be?

I don't doubt for a moment that at least a part, and possibly a large part, of the popularity of songs like "Lily of Laguna" is dependent upon a nostalgia felt by many people for times past. In England (where only in recent years has colour been a source of anguish) this nostalgia is not for some lost or dying Southern States' way of life (as presumably it might be felt in parts of the United States) but rather for a world of tranquility and order, dimly sensed as once existing in a time of the minstrel shows and pierrots. It is the sort of nostalgia John Osborne pilloried, but, in his dramatisation of Colonel Redfern, seemed paradoxically to be hankering after in *Look Back in Anger* ten years ago.

Leslie Stuart was English, but created a world of imagination largely peopled by coloured men and women from the Southern United States. He was not alone in this (nor was this his only preoccupation), but he expressed this imaginary dream world particularly attractively, and the songs were sympathetically presented by the American, Eugene Stratton. But has this dream world anything more permanent to offer than that of "Champagne Charlie"? Something, certainly, for Stuart was undoubtedly a much more sensitive craftsman than were the authors of the songs about drink. Stuart's scores were prepared with great care. He always seeks some pointed relationship between words and music; special effects (such as the echo of "Is Yer Mammie Always With Ye" and the shepherdess's call in "Lily of Laguna") and the extended passages of music for dancing are part of a clearly integrated whole.

In recordings made by Stratton it is noticable how closely he observes what are, for music-hall songs, relatively detailed musical instructions. The description, "Shepherdess's call up the mountain," for the oboe obbligato which follows the verse in "Lily of Laguna" may seem ridiculous, but the music is delicate rather than tritely imitative. It is a genuine musical interpretation of the situation in the song, in the same way that, as all accounts suggest, Stratton's soft-shoe dancing was choreographically an apt interpretation of the song. Clearly we have in "Lily of Laguna", and in Stuart's songs generally, a degree of conscious artistry quite different from that found in most music-hall songs. Perhaps it could be said that the others wrote songs while Stuart produced compositions.

"Lily of Laguna" is exceptional in its period in that, though full of sentiment, it avoids the worst excesses. It is one of the rare love songs of the time that is still acceptable as such even if, because of our changed attitudes to "coon" songs, we must make some allowances. Stuart by no means always avoided sentimentality (see the extract from the song he wrote for Vesta Tilley, "Sweetheart May", on page 190) and, as "Soldiers of the Queen" indicates, he could be as jingoistic as G. W. Hunt.

The reason that sentiment does not become ridiculous in "Lily of Laguna" is to be found in Stuart's management of tone. I don't think we doubt the singer's sincerity, yet we are kept a little at a distance. This detachment is effected verbally and musically. There is, first of all, a slight touch of humour (although not the astringent undercutting kind of Cockney songs) in the references to being a black sheep and escaping father's "esscortch." The conversation, though less well managed than in "The Future Mrs. 'Awkins," also helps to promote this sense of detachment (especially "Kern't believe ye") and the dotted crochet-quaver (or dotted quaver, semi-quaver) musical pattern has the effect of breaking up the rhythm so that an over-languid, too sentimental effect is avoided. Finally, in singing the song, Stratton, and many who have followed him, have adopted a caressing tone. Instead of seeming over-confidential, as it might have done, this has helped to undercut the emotion. The sentiment is worn lightly, as it were.

"Lily of Laguna" then, though it derives part of its continued success from the nostalgia it evokes for many people, also has qualities that do not rest solely on such slippery ground. Is it possible to go on to say, as does Macqueen-Pope, that Stuart is probably the greatest of music-hall songwriters? I don't think so, although I doubt if there is any better musician—any better composer—among the writers of songs popular on the halls. Macqueen-Pope correctly points to the influence of church music on Leslie Stuart; and, indeed, we are often not too far from "The Lost Chord" in some of his songs. It is this inheritance that gives Stuart's songs a certain sobriety, and he has also something of the musicianship of a Sullivan. Unfortunately, in this field, this is nearly as great a condemnation as it is a virtue. Stuart's songs may never seem carelessly thrown together—thought and craftsmanship may always be apparent—but too often what is lacking is the kind of complexity of tone found in songs such as "Waiting at the Church" and "Jeerusalem," together with that rare kind of relationship to a world of experience, real or imaginative, that will seem valid in some age other than its own. His songs lack the classical qualities without having the compensatory virtues of songs such as "The 'Ouses In Between."

The extent to which Stuart's work is removed from the kind of song that still has vitality can also be seen in two of his exceptional songs: "The Banshee," a song based upon the intriguing idea of a coloured boy cast up by shipwreck on the shores of Donegal and taken for a fairy man, and "I May Be Crazy," a "Mexican Romance" in which the singer is crazy enough to try to see his girl with a posse hot on his heels.

The initial idea of "The Banshee" is excellent, but Stuart doesn't quite seem to know what to do with it. As so often in Stuart's work, the effect—in this case the banshee's howl—is carefully controlled, and there is a nice opposition between the perplexity of the Negro boy taken for a fairy and the superstition of those who so imagine him. Yet the song is static. It is not too absurd to equate it with a play by Maeterlinck such as *Interior*. In the song the difficulty arises because Stuart (perhaps unconsciously) is imagining a real situation in his dream world, but has found no satisfactory resolution. It is an interesting song and would repay more detailed attention, but it does not make the most of the initial imaginative idea.

"I May Be Crazy" is described at length by Macqueen-Pope:

> The whole song was drama, it had an urge, a
> breathlessness of words and music admirably
> suited to the situation . . . The music matched
> the tensely gripping drama and the mad, violent,
> hopeless dance of abandon which followed was
> a very miracle, all the more grim for its silence.
> [Music is provided for this dance, so presumably
> when Macqueen-Pope saw it, it was danced with-
> out accompaniment.] It ended with the posse,
> pistols in hand, dragging him away, as he wrenched
> himself round in their grasp to give one last de-
> spairing glance of dumb, stricken grief at the house
> of his loved one and throw out his arms in a mute
> appeal.

One might expect from this description another "Sam Hall," though perhaps one more crudely melodramatic. Clearly the whole performance made a great appeal to Macqueen-Pope, but I doubt if "I May Be Crazy" could ever be quite as dramatic as it seemed to him when he wrote this, nearly fifty years after seeing Stratton's performance. The music of the song is singularly inappropriate for such **stark** drama, for it jogs along with surprising equanimity—an equanimity which is brought out fully in Stratton's recording of the song. "I May Be Crazy" is much more a song of the importunate flirt than the desparate lover. The "real" situation with which it is concerned cannot be contained within such a dream-world treatment. The inadequacy of "I May Be Crazy" reveals the inhibiting weakness that lies at the core of even the most successful of Stuart's achievements in this dream world.

Possibly the description of this song on an early five-inch Zonophone record of about 1900 (0-42008) provides an apt, if not too reliable, comment. No singer's name is given, but the song is provided with a succinct description: "I May Be Crazy, But I Love You (Comic)."

When I Take My Morning Promenade

Sung by Marie Lloyd. Written and Composed by A. J. Mills and Bennett Scott. Copyright: B. Feldman & Co., Ltd.

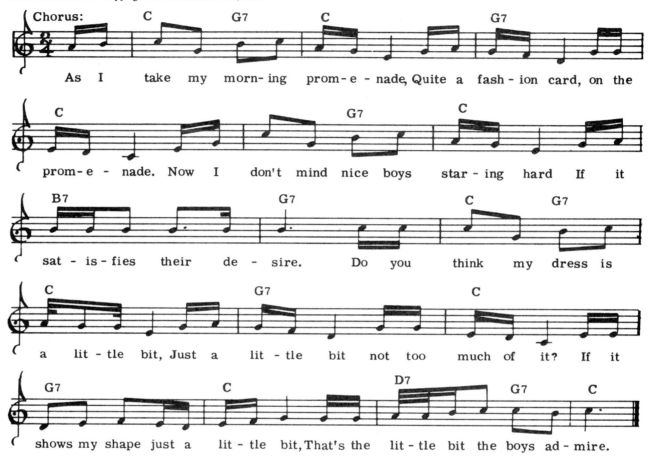

Since Mother Eve in the Garden long ago,
Started the fashion, fashion's been a fashion.
She wore a strip that has mystified the priests,
Still every season brought a change of green.
She'd stare if she came to town,
What would Mother Eve think of my new
   Parisian gown.

CHORUS:
As I take my morning promenade,
Quite a fashion card, on the promenade.
Now I don't mind nice boys staring hard
If it satisfies their desire.
Do you think my dress is a little bit,
Just a little bit—not too much of it?
If it shows my shape just a little bit,
That's the little bit the boys admire.

Fancy the girls in the prehistoric days,
Had to wear a bearskin to cover up their fair skin.
Lately Salome has danced to be sure,
Wearing just a row of beads and not much more.
Fancy me dressing like that, too!
I'm sure "The Daily Mirror" man would want
   an interview.

I've heard that grandmother wore a crinoline;
Then came the bustle—Oh! wasn't that a tussle.
Women were tied up and loaded up with dress,
But fashion now decrees that she must wear
   much less.
Each year her costume grows more brief,
I wonder when we'll get back to the good
   old-fashioned leaf.

To many, Marie Lloyd was the greatest female star of the music halls. To some she even eclipsed Dan Leno. Max Beerbohm paid tribute to Leno at his death; T. S. Eliot wrote on Marie Lloyd when she died and his essay has been reprinted many times in *Selected Essays*. I have no wish to belittle what is a personal appreciation of a remarkable artist, but two points might reasonably be made about what Eliot says. He remarks that though he had always admired the genius of Marie Lloyd, he did not think he had always appreciated its unique quality, for, he says:

> No other comedian succeeded so well in
> giving expression to the life of that audience,
> in raising it to a kind of art. It was, I think, this
> capacity for expressing the soul of the people that
> made Marie Lloyd unique, and that made her
> audiences, even when they joined in the chorus,
> not so much hilarious as happy.

Marie Lloyd was not, I think, unique in this respect. Other artistes, including Chevalier, Formby Sr., and Elen, were able to "express the soul of the people," and were able, also, to raise it to "a kind of art." Furthermore the attitudes to life, and the sense of values these performers revealed in "expressing the soul of the people" were often different from the attitudes and values of the *theatre de boulevard*. This Marie Lloyd herself discovered to her cost.

Eliot remarks that "the attitude of audiences toward Marie Lloyd was different from their attitude toward any other of their favourites of that day, and this difference represents the difference in her art." A little later, referring to Nellie Wallace's capacity to subdue a jeering and hostile East End audience, he says:

> But I have never known Marie Lloyd to be
> confronted by this kind of hostility; in any
> case, the feeling of the vast majority of the
> audience was so manifestly on her side, that
> no objector would have dared to lift his voice.

Now as Eliot was writing an essay in tribute, not a history or biography, he may fairly be excused, but this statement about Marie Lloyd is factually wrong.

It is evident from George Gamble's essay on music halls published in *The Halls* (about 1898) that Marie Lloyd did not please everyone. Gamble devotes two full pages to Chevalier but this is all he has to say of Marie Lloyd (and Alec Hurley, her second husband):

> Mr. Alec Hurley I have not seen; but I am told
> that he is good.
> Miss Marie Lloyd I *have* seen; and I am told that
> *she* is good.

More illuminating is a story told by her friend, Chance Newton, a music-hall writer and critic of long standing.

Chance Newton's own account is better than any summary. Marie Lloyd met him at the old Tivoli one day and the following conversation ensued:

> "I'm going to the Paragon next Monday. It's
> the first time I've ever appeared there. I reckon

I shall have to 'lay it on a bit thick' down White-chapel way, what?"

"My dear girl," I replied, "I marvel at *you*—an East End native—making such a statement to *me*, with all my inside knowledge of East End shows and show-goers.

"Now speaking from that experience," I continued, "and from the manner in which I have seen Hoxton, Whitechapel, and Mile End play-goers and music-hall goers treat 'blue' singers and undressed actresses, I warn you that if you dare to sing at the Paragon any of your very 'shady' songs you are now singing in the West End, that East End audience will balloon you off the stage!"

Marie Lloyd would have none of this, and Newton records what happened when she did resort to what earlier he calls her "ceruleanism of song" (and for which she had been warned by the management of the Pavilion in the West End of London):

As I entered [the Paragon] I heard a noise. It was the sound of an audience giving a not too favourable reception to our wonderful little pal. In fact so unfavourable was it that Marie dashed off in a mixed state of rage and weeping.

Happily she pulled herself together and returned to give one of her cleverest character studies.

Newton's style is odd to our ears and time might have blurred certain details, but it is likely that the main points of this story are correct for he greatly admired Marie Lloyd and they were very good friends. (Macqueen-Pope also records this incident in his biography of Marie Lloyd.) There can be little doubt that Marie Lloyd was caught between two different sets of values, and the reaction of the East End audience to the "ceruleanism" acceptable to the more sophisticated West End audience was plain and sharp, beloved though Marie Lloyd was. The reaction was not unlike that of certain Australian miners to Sumner Locke Elliott's *Rusty Bugles*, after the Second World War. They considered (as did the government of New South Wales) that such words as "bloody" and "bastard" (in context) were not fit to be included in a play about the Australian Army that women might attend.[1] How is this reaction to be explained? Why did the East End audience react so violently? Bawdy and innuendo were hardly unknown to them.

The basic reason is because of a confusion toward what is proper. Where no absolute standard of decorum exists, what is fitting in one situation may be inappropriate in another. Thus the Australian miners did not wish their wives to hear in the context of the public theatre what they could not avoid hearing in daily life. Marie Lloyd's innuendo was hardly likely to be any worse than that offered by other entertainers, but what was acceptable from one kind of performer was repugnant from someone as idolised as Marie Lloyd, regarded virtually as the epitome of what the East End audience considered to be best in itself. However popular Marie Lloyd became with West End audiences, she would not seem to them to epitomise themselves, and what she implied would

[1]See Appendix III of *Towards an Australian Drama*, Leslie Rees, Angus & Robertson, Sydney, 1953.

not conflict with any idealistic concept. Thus each audience had different values and different standards. So far as Marie Lloyd was concerned, "ceruleanism" was at issue, but it might equally have been possible to offend such an audience on political, religious, or social grounds. We have two different ways of looking at life, two different interpretations of the conventions of life, each a product of its own society; and the music hall by and large reflects the less sophisticated of these ways of experiencing life. This can be a severe restriction, and it can result in banality and triviality; often in music hall this is the case. But the music hall can express a different way of looking at certain aspects of life, a different kind of experience of life, that is idiosyncratic and worthwhile, having no exact comparable equivalent in the more sophisticated world.[1]

"When I Take My Morning Promenade" might be described as a fleshly song. It rejoices in the delights of the womanly shape. The words are innocent enough, but it would not be difficult to present the song salaciously. The singer has to get the utmost out of the song without being offensive to the audience.

It could be argued that the song is deliberately provocative, raising hopes it will not fulfil; and, of course, up to a point it is a come-on song. It would be more accurate, however, to regard the song as expressing in down-to-earth manner the attractions of women. The taking of the morning promenade is presented for what it really is without any equivocation. Fashion is clearly part of sexual attraction and is not itself dressed up to be anything else.

What we have displayed before us is a society lady of fashion (or, at least, a popular stage version of fashion, cutting the dress a little lower here and a little higher there) presenting herself in the tone and with the attitude of the world from which *the singer* springs. In Marie Lloyd's treatment, fashion is made to serve a specific human purpose and is subservient to that purpose. It is not seen, as in the high society which she is aping, as fashion for its own sake. The difference is important, and the popular dramatic view is the more honest of the two. The singer has the emphasis in the right place—on the exposure of what allures, not on fashionableness itself. The values, provocative or not, seem well and objectively judged.

---

[1]It is only fair to mention that Marie Lloyd has often been defended against charges of blueness. Much of the difficulty of ascertaining the true facts arises from a confusion of terms. Clarkson Rose has said that she was "saucy—yes, Rabelaisian—yes; but never dirty." But there are authorities which consider Rabelais deserving of condemnation.

Every Little Movement

Sung by Marie Lloyd. Written and Composed by
K. Hoschna and O. A. Haverbach. Copyright: 1910,
M. Witmark & Sons, and B. Feldman & Co., Ltd.

Chorus:

And every little movement has a meaning of its own,
Every little movement tells a tale. When she walks in
dainty hobbles, At the back round here, there's a kind of
wibble wobble; And she glides like this, Then the
Johnnies follow in her trail, 'Cos when she turns her head like so, something's
going, don't you know, Every little movement tells a tale.

Up to the West End, right in the best end,
Straight from the country came Miss Maudie Brown.
Father a curate, but couldn't endure it,
That's why the lady's residing in town.
Twelve months ago her modest self felt quite sublime
—To sit on a fellow's knee who's been in all the grime!
And if you should want a kiss,
She'd droop her eyes like this,
But now she droops them just one at a time.

102

CHORUS:
And every little movement has a meaning of its own,
Every little movement tells a tale.
When she walks in dainty hobbles,
At the back round here, there's a kind of wibble-wobble;
And she glides like this,
Then the Johnnies follow in her trail,
'Cos when she turns her head like so,
Something's going, don't you know,
Every little movement tells a tale.

Down by the blue sea, cute as she could be,
Maudie would go for her dip every day.
Maudie has an eye for the boys, Oh my!
And it happens that Reggie was passing that way.
When Reggie saw her he fell into a trance,
He too is going bathing for here now, here's a chance.
She didn't smile or frown,
Just threw her signal down!
Then slyly shrugged her shoulders with a glance.

CHORUS:
And every little movement has a meaning of its own,
Every little movement tells a tale.
When she dashed into the ocean,
Reggie kept close by for to know her
Maudie tried to swim:
"Oh I'm here," said Reggie, "if you fail,"
And in less than half a wink,
Maudie dear commenced to sink,
Every little movement tells a tale.

Congratulations, such celebrations,
Bertie and Gertie have just tied the knot.
Both at the party, all gay and hearty,
And noticed the bridegroom looks anxious, eh what?
When friends and relatives depart their different ways,
Alone with the girlie of his heart.
And once again he turned the lights down low,
She looked at him like so,
Then shyly with her wedding ring she played.

CHORUS:
And every little movement has a meaning of its own,
Every little movement tells a tale.
When alone no words they utter,
But when midnight chimed, then their hearts begin to flutter.
And she yawned like this,
And stretches out her arm so frail,
And her hubby full of love,
Looks at her and points above,
Every little movement tells a tale.

There is a long tradition of songs about young maidens who come up from the country as sweet modest creatures to flower (or, to some alternate fate) in the great big city. The classic comic-pathetic "She Was Poor But She Was Honest" is one such; so is "And Her Golden Hair Was Hanging Down Her Back," and also the last song in this volume, "Heaven Will Protect an Honest Girl." "Every Little Movement"(as does the third song sung by Marie Lloyd to be given here, "I've Never Lost My Last Train Yet") depends upon this tradition. "Every Little Movement," like "When I Take My Morning Promenade," has scope for provocative movement by the performer, while "My Last Train" relies upon verbal innuendo. As is very common is music-hall songs, especially those sung by Marie Lloyd, the words are innocent but could easily be given another significance. Thus Marie Lloyd's "Twiggy Vous" could be sung in all innocence by a Victorian lady in the drawing room but rouse roars of knowing laughter in the halls.

The scores of Marie Lloyd's songs, and even her recordings, do little to suggest how immensely their singer was admired. "Every Little Movement" (an American song, incidentally), like her other songs printed here, reveals a wholehearted acceptance of relations between the sexes: there is no pretence of presenting sexual attraction as something other than it is; but there are no deeper insights into the way of life from which Marie Lloyd came, nor anything more than superficial observation of the kind of life she describes. These three Marie Lloyd songs present a scene, or tell briefly of incidents, which have but a tenuous relationship to reality. Up to a point this is merely to say that by the standards of realistic convention they fall short compared to, say, Chevalier's or Elen's songs. But also, they do not create an imaginative world of their own nor do they reveal that delight in language found in so many music-hall songs.

It is a little strange that Marie Lloyd has left relatively few songs that have had an independent existence without her—relatively few, that is, when the astonishing reputation she had in her lifetime is taken into account. Possibly the two best-known are "My Old Man Said Follow The Van (but I Dillied, I Dallied)" and "A Little or What You Fancy Does You Good." It is noticeable that both of these songs are drawn from the life around her. There are a number of such songs that might be well worth rescuing from obscurity, of which one of the most attractive is "The Coster's Christening," with its delightful line, "The baby, it was crying like an angel" —sung without any trace of facetious humour. Some of her songs had only topical significance. "The Piccadilly Trot" (about 1912) was a reply to the American import, "The Turkey Trot"; and, like most music-hall stars, she had her war songs. But many of her songs lack the vitality they once had because they depended on her presence to give them life. They enabled her to give expression to an attitude to sexuality (and it is this that is the most interesting characteristic of the three of her songs given here), but they need her presence to embody that attitude.

Some of Marie Lloyd's recordings were made very early in the days of commercial recording and it is understandable that the words are at times difficult to pick out. However, even in some of her later records, her words are less clear than one could wish, for she has a bad habit of running one word into another and of distorting consonants. Nevertheless, the sound of her voice, strong and with plenty of bite, gives an impression of cheerful gusto appropriate to songs of fleshly delight.

"Every Little Movement," as she presents it in the recording from which the words and music printed here have been taken, is in part concerned with Maudie Brown and her movements; but then, rather awkwardly, it shifts to Bertie and Gertie. The names themselves evoke a kind of social whirl about which many songs were written at the beginning of the century, but which now strikes us as particularly hollow and pretentious. It was later to be deflated in songs sung by Vesta Tilley, Morny Cash, and George Formby Sr., among others. Although this world is meaningless, in describing it there is an occasional realistic detail—such as the playing with the wedding ring—which undercuts the fantasy. In the main, however, "Every Little Movement" endeavours to evoke the dream world of a gay social whirl in a manner not unlike that used by George Leybourne and the Great Vance. Because the basis of this dream world is orientated on sex instead of on luxurious liquors, the song retains an element of attraction that its setting would otherwise deny it.

I've Never Lost My Last Train Yet

Sung by Marie Lloyd. Written by George Rollit; Composed
by George Le Brunn. Copyright: Bowerman & Co.

I'm a mo-dest lit-tle mai-den from the coun-try, Where I'm
liv-ing with my mo-ther quite a-lone; And it's on-ly ve-ry sel-dom she allows me to be-take my-self to Lon-don on my own; For in
town I have a sort of se-cond cou-sin, Who en-joys to take me round to see the
sights; And he al-ways comes and meets me At the sta-tion, and he treats me To the
var-ious Met-ro-pol-i-tan de-lights. Yes, there's noth-ing half so sweet as the
days on which we meet, For he's quite the ni-cest boy I've ev-er

met; But al-though I love a lark In the day and in the dark, I have ne-ver lost my last train yet, oh no! I have ne-ver lost my last train yet!

I'm a modest little maiden from the country,
Where I'm living with my mother quite alone;
And it's only very seldom she allows me
To betake myself to London "on my own":
For in town I have a sort of second cousin,
Who enjoys to take me round to see the sights;
    And he always comes and meets me
      At the station and he treats me
To the various Metropolitan delights.

CHORUS:
Yes, there's nothing half so sweet
As the days on which we meet,
For he's quite the nicest boy I've ever met;
But although I love a lark
In the day and in the dark,
I have never lost my last train yet, Oh No!
I have never lost my last train yet!

I admit I'm very fond of nature's beauty,
Of the flowers and the birdies in the air,
And the chickens and the ducks who gather
    round me,
And the cattle who regard me with a stare;
Now this sort of thing, no doubt is very
    charming,
But it's really getting very, very slow,
    And I'm longing for sensations,
      Such as gentle dissipations,
Which I always find in London when I go.

CHORUS:
For I've experienced what it is
To have quaffed a glass of "fiz",
When you're supping with a gay and giddy set,
And I've joined with one and all
In a Covent Garden ball,
But I've never lost my last train yet, Oh No!
I have never lost my last train yet.

Now although I am as heartless as a lambkin
That has never heard of mint sauce in its "puff",
I am getting somewhat sick of rural beauty,
Or in other words I've had about enough.
I should love to have a flat in Piccadilly
And to go and do exactly as I choose,
    For had I my habitation
      In a West End situation,
Then of course, I would not have a train to lose.

CHORUS:
Yes, I've learnt to know the bliss
Of a stolen little kiss,
When you heave a sigh and softly murmer,
    "Pet!"
As you gaze into his face,
Wrapt in amorous embrace,
But I've never lost my last train yet, Oh No!
I've never lost my last train yet.

Now a week or two ago I asked my cousin
To escort me to Boulogne—just for the day;
Very soon we were on board the *Marguerite*,
    boys,
And we had a fair old beano on the way.
At Boulogne we found the fun was fast and furious,
And of ways to pass the time there was no lack;
    We were feeling, oh so happy,
      When I said, "Look here, old chappy,
Don't you think it's time that we were getting
    back?"

CHORUS:
For when looking at the clock
I received a dreadful shock,
On discovering that the sun had gone and set.
So a telegram I wrote:
"Dear Mama, I've missed the boat!"
But I haven't lost my last train yet, Oh No!
I haven't lost my last train yet.

107

The surface meaning of "I've Never Lost My Last Train Yet" is innocent enough, but the innuendo (akin to that which relates stages of lovemaking to stations on a local railway line) is plain. Taking a flat in the West End of London with such a "sort of second cousin" in the offing is clearly indicative of the implication of not having a train to lose any more. The lyric runs better and with greater internal consistency than do those of the other two Marie Lloyd songs given here, and the balance between what it is felt ought to be done and what it would be pleasant to do, is carefully held. This is clearly shown in the last lines of the first chorus, where what, on the surface, is a *non sequitur,* is logical in its underlying implication:

> But though I love a lark
> In the day and in the dark,
> I have never lost my last train yet, Oh No!

In another of Marie Lloyd's songs in which the country girl (in this case a farmer's daughter) comes to London, there is a somewhat similar innuendo. The song is called "What Did She Know About Railways?" and the chorus goes:

> She arrived at Euston by the midnight train,
> But when she got to the wicket, there was someone wanted
>   to punch her ticket.
> The guards and the porters came round her by the score,
> And she told them all that she'd never had a ticket
>   punched before.

The second verse concludes:

> She said, "Thou punch my ticket and I'll punch thee on thy nose!"
> But what did she know about railways?

The situations in "I've Never Lost My Last Train Yet" are adequately set up, and there is a considerable amount of detail worked into the song. Occasionally there is an effective wry humour:

> And I'm longing for sensations
> Such as gentle dissipations.

By undercutting, the epithet provides an amusing qualification to the idea of hectic dissipation. It is not clear why a lambkin is heartless (perhaps the idea of innocence ought to be conveyed), and in the last chorus something is a little astray. I can't imagine what has been happening that it is necessary to look at a clock to see that the sun has gone and set! On the whole, however, the song is better contrived than many songs of this kind: it certainly runs better than "Every Little Movement."

A certain amount of rather superficial contrast is revealed between country and town, but this does not go very deep. What is of more interest is the extent to which this song dramatises the effort to grab as much as possible without losing that vital last train. Is there any irony in the way in which material and moral values are balanced one against the other, particularly in the end of the third verse? It is just possible that the song has an element of self-criticism in it, although I doubt very much whether it was written, sung, or received with this in mind.

It is sadly ironical that Marie Lloyd, who gave the public much pleasure and was so willing to help those in misfortune, never enjoyed very much happiness in her private life. Each of her three marriages was unsuccessful, the last one disastrously so. Her end was painful and forlorn. She collapsed on the stage singing the last lines of a song unfortunately only too appropriate to her circumstances—a third song of hers that has lived on—"I'm one of the Ruins That Cromwell Knocked Abaht a Bit." It was her last public appearance: she could not make the second performance on that day; and, three days later, she was dead.

One of the Deathless Army

Sung by Little Tich. Words by T. W. Thurban; Music by
Gilbert Wells, Will Terry, and V. R. Gill. Copyright:
Francis, Day & Hunter, Ltd.

Old Brig-ade." If ev-er I go to war, I'll drive the en-e-my bar-my, Hi, Hi! Ne-ver say die! I'm one of the death-less ar-my.

I am a bolger sold—I mean I'm a soldier bold,
I'm not so young as I used to be before I got so old.
I am a regular toff I am, I am, I say I am;
But you can't tell what's inside the jar by the label on the jam.

CHORUS:
For I'm a soldier, a Territorial.
The girls will say when I'm on parade
"There's one of the boys of the Old Brigade."
If ever I go to war, I'll drive the enemy barmy,
Hi, Hi! Never say die!
I'm one of the deathless army.

PATTER: *(to pathetic music): Would you like me to tell you the
story, sir, of the horribleness of war? Well, it was half-past
six in the morning, sir, when the clock struck five-to-four—
there was something went wrong with the works, sir, but the
enemy wanted a fight. Why, they lay with our right on their left,
sir, and we lay with our left on their right. And I wanted a
Turkish Bath, sir, but the colonel said, "Lad, there's
no hope." For the drummer boy's drunk all the water and the
bugler's swallowed the soap. I lay down and shrieked in my
anguish, but the colonel said, "Lad, never mind, why, you
haven't got on any trousers!" Huh! So I went in and pulled
down the blind. Then the bugler tootled his tooter, and I
knew that the foeman was nigh, so I rushed out to buy some
tobacco, when a cannon ball flopped in my eye. You know, I
could scarcely see for a moment and I thought it was very
unkind. Then the colonel's wife dropped in to see me and said,
"Er, shall we, er, pull down the blind?" Then the enemy
clustered around us, and the colonel went clean off his
chump. And the horses drew horse and stampeded, and the camels
had all got the hump. Well I was having a whiskey and soda, sir,
when a shot struck me, er, somewhere behind. As I could not
pull it out in the street, sir, I went in and pulled down the
blind. And the shells lay around me in thousands, and still
they continued to drop. So I payed for the dozen I'd eaten
and walked out of the oyster shop. And the shots they were
buzzing around me, and one nearly blew off my head. There
were cannons to right of me, cannons to left of me—so what
did I do? Went in off the red.*

Chorus

111

Little Tich

Arthur Orton was a very large butcher who came from Wagga Wagga in Australia to claim the fortune due to Roger Tichborne, thought to be lost at sea. The The claim was contested in a lengthy trial and eventually Orton was ignominiously convicted of perjury. Harry Relph was a very small man who first billed himself in 1880 as the Little Tichborne, spent some time as a minstrel, and then rose to great fame in many countries as "Little Tich"—and thus was introduced the word "tich" into the English language.

Little Tich did not so much sing songs as present characters, and he was able to do this in several languages, becoming as popular on the Continent as in England. What is presented here is a shortened version of one of his acts taken from a recording made before the First Great War. Sketchy though it is, it gives some indication of a particularly interesting kind of act. The verse and chorus serve to introduce and to round off the patter which forms the bulk of the act. This absurd patter Little Tich presented in a sustained, declamatory style, but the absurdity of the language was allowed to creep into the voice, effectively undercutting its quasi-serious style. The act burlesques the new Territorial (part-time) Army, and in later years the "deathless army" came to be associated with the British Expeditionary Force of the Great War. Another song which poked fun at amateur soldiers was "Since Poor Father Joined the Territorials," for a verse of which I am indebted to Terence Spencer:

> Since poor father joined the Territorials,
> Ours is a happy little home!
> He wakes us up in the middle of the night
> And says we all must be prepared to fight!
> He puts poor mother in the dust-bin to stand on sentry-guard;
> And me and brother Bert,
> In his little flannel shirt,
> He keeps drilling in the old back yard!

The popular drama has always found a place for nonsense. It is not difficult to find a relationship between the humour of Little Tich's song and that of The Goon Show, a popular B.B.C. Radio Show of the 1950s which featured Peter Sellers, Spike Milligan, and Harry Secombe. The sources of the humour are chiefly illogicality and absurdity, repetition and innuendo, and playing with language. In Little Tich's recording the act is presented straight, as if it were a natural and logical account, the absurdity not being stressed. Only the most subtle exaggeration and the slightest awareness of the comic implications suggest to the listener a guying of the dramatic monologue of the period. The only change in this approach occurs when the continuity is broken by a "direct address" to the audience in the line, "You know, I could scarcely see for a moment and I thought it was very unkind." I put "direct address" in quotes because this description is obviously anomalous. The whole act is delivered directly across the footlights to the audience. This change of direction occurs when the continuity of the act is broken by Little Tich speaking as himself, as it were, instead of in the persona of a Territorial soldier—a good example of the way in which a performer on the popular stage can slip out of, and back into, the persona being presented in a way that is not possible in the legitimate drama of the *theatre de boulevard.*

Willson Disher has remarked that the clue to Little Tich's philosophy was "the jest at tribulation," and this can be seen in "I'm a Territorial." Disher continues:

> He rarely saw the jest off-stage. He was painfully
> conscious of his physical peculiarities, of the freakish
> extra finger on each of his hands. Nor was he happy
> in exciting laughter. He wanted higher tribute than
> that. He wanted to be praised for his art, to be taken
> seriously—a desire not altogether unlike Leno's
> ambition to play Hamlet.[1]

[1] "Winkles and Champagne, p. 44

The Fire Was Burning Hot

Sung by T. E. Dunville. Written and Composed by T. W. Connor. Copyright: Bowerman & Co.

Our gallant men were fast asleep
    Awaiting duty's call,
When someone brought the fearful news
    That mesmerised us all.
A chimney pot was smoking
    Only ten miles further on,
And if we didn't hurry up,
    The beer would all be gone.

PATTER:
*I forgot to ask where the fire was,
but wrote a letter at once to the turncock, and
sent a man round to the wheelwright's to see
when the engine would be finished. As it
happened, the horses were out doing a funeral
job. When they came home, I had to take
'em to the farriers, and after that we made a
start. When we got there we found the fire
was on the fourth storey, and our ladder
only reached to the second. So we had to wait
till the fire got down, or call again to-morrow.
Captain gave us three weeks to consider and
in the meantime—*

Chorus

The fire was burning hot,
    And the water was perishing cold;
Our gallant lads all parched and dry,
    Watching from the pub close by;
And when the fire was out,
    Like heroes they behaved,
And every soul in that empty house
    That didn't get burnt got saved!

We searched in all the jewellers' shops,
    But no plug could we find;
Our Captain shouted, "Cheer up, boys,
    We've left the hose behind!"
Then up the gutter spout he rushed,
    His whiskers tied in knots,
And rubbed some hokey-pokey on
    To cool the chimney pots.

PATTER:
*Wonderful man our Captain—got
three medals and a dog-bite. Made a patent
fire-escape, all out of his own head. Swears in
fourteen languages. He only left us once while
he went to have his boots cleaned. Then somebody went and put hot water on the fire,
which, of course, made it ten times worse.
And in the meantime—*

Chorus

At last we got the fire alight,
    And swallowed all the smoke,
We couldn't reach the windows, so
    We smashed up all the coke;
We cheered ourselves—with bated breath,
    We knew not what about,
And never left till all the pubs
    Were fairly gutted out

PATTER:
*Then came the welcome order—
single men go home, married men stop out
for a change. I was one of 'em, and it was hot
work—stopping out all night, but duty's duty,
whether it is or not, and besides—*

Chorus
We drew our faithful choppers out
    And put 'em back again,
And thanked our lucky stars we'd all
    Got water on the brain;
Our fireproof whiskers turned to (h)air
    As the roof turned inside out;
We shut our eyes, and looked and looked—
    Like idiots, no doubt.

Chorus

After a hard beginning and several false starts, T.E. Dunville developed an idiosyncratic style which made him very popular. But the ill-luck he had in starting dogged him after the Great War when the halls were in decline. He felt he was losing his touch, and in 1924 drowned himself in the Thames. Like many entertainers he used a name other than his own, Dunville being a brand of whiskey. (Perhaps the most intriguing stage name is that adopted by Vernon Watson, supposedly taken from the injunction pasted up in the "No Smoking" compartments of railway carriages: Nosmo King.)

Dunville had a fine line in nonsense and some of his songs were not dissimilar in style from Dickens's Mr. Jingle.* J.B. Booth quotes the song of Little Billie Bates:

> Little Billie Bates,
> Fastened on his skates,
> Skated when the ice was thin.
> Suddenly a crack—
> Laid him on his back.
> Little Billie Bates went in—
> And the verdict was:
>
> Little boy—
> Pair of skates—
> Hole in ice—
> Heaven's gates.

Dunville also had an act which holds interest outside the story of the halls. At the time of the Boer War he presented himself as Brimstone Chapel in the song, "The War Correspondent," a comic version of Winston Churchill in this capacity. In such songs (as in "The Fire Was Burning Hot"), the tune was less important than the words and the manner of their delivery.

Good absurdity requires something more than the putting together of a sequence of *non-sequiturs*. "The Fire Was Burning Hot" gets off to a good start. "Our gallant lads were fast asleep/ Awaiting duty's call" is at one level logical and rational—it is possible to await the ringing of a fire bell while fast asleep, but expectation demands that gallant lads await the call of duty while wide a-wake. Similarly with the chimney pot smoking only ten miles away. The absurdity is not gross; it is a combination of rational statement, deflation (it is only a chimney pot that is on fire), and paradox (only ten miles—as if it were paces).

The chorus, like the verses, has short, staccato lines; and it uses a variety of verbal devices to produce the comic effect. It is noticeable that, though absurd, it has a kind of logic, chiefly of association: fire/hot—water/cold—lads/dry—watching/ pubs—fire (out)/(then) behaved as heroes—all saved. The humour of the last two lines is based not only upon absurdity but also upon logic, for inevitably every soul in an empty house would be saved, more particularly if all avoided the flames.

Not all the verses are as good. Some of the lines, such as "His whiskers tied in knots" and "We smashed up all the coke," owe their existence to the exigencies of rhyme rather than to inspiration or "logic." In the third and fourth verses there is an extension of the comic techniques. "We cheered ourselves— with bated breath/We knew not what about" neatly takes off on the melodramatic and the double use of "looked" is an amusing example of zeugma.

The patter is better than that for most of the songs given in this collection, and often comes up to the standard of Little Tich's in "I'm a Territorial." There is an imaginative touch about some of the absurdities. A captain with three medals and a dog-bite is one thing, but one who has only left his men to have his boots cleaned is quite another. And there is just the trace of a kick about "Duty's duty, whether it is or not."

"The Fire was Burning Hot" was written and composed by T.W. Connor who was also responsible for George Formby Sr.'s "The Man Was a Stranger To Me."

*Dickens was not the originator of the telegram-style even in his own period. It is, for example, the mode of speech used by Dr. Pother in Charles Dibdin's *The Farmer's Wife:* Make a capital story. Farmer and wife - rural affection - husband abroad - wife at home - intriguing baronet - elopement - red-hot poker - Old Nick in the chimney - down he comes - fat in the fire - and the devil hauled over the coals. (Act III Sc iv)

My Fiddle Is My Sweetheart

Sung by G. H. Chirgwin, and composed by him; Written
by Harry Hunter. Copyright: Francis, Day & Hunter, Ltd.

My fid - dle is my sweet-heart and — I'm her faith - ful
beau; I take her to my bo - som, Be - cause I love her
so. I clasp her gent - ly round her neck, Her vo - cal chords I
press, I ask her if she loves me, and she an - swers, "Yes, yes,
yes!" She'll sing at ev - 'ry sea - son, De - cem - ber or in
June, But must have (ro - sin) rea - son, or will not sing in
tune. It's not un - til I coax her well that she'll re - veal her
charms, But she will sing her sweet - est song when once she's in my arms. My

fid - dle is my sweet-heart, And I'm her faith - ful beau; I

take her to my bo - som, Be - cause I love her so.

My fiddle is my sweetheart,
And I'm her faithful beau;
I take her to my bosom,
Because I love her so.
I clasp her gently round her neck,
Her vocal chords I press,
I ask her if she loves me, and
She answers, "Yes, yes, yes!"
She'll sing at ev'ry season,
December or in June,
But must have (*rosin*) reason,
Or will not sing in tune.
It's not until I coax her well
That she'll reveal her charms,
But she will sing her sweetest song,
When once she's in my arms.

CHORUS:
My fiddle is my sweetheart,
And I'm her faithful beau;
I take her to my bosom,
Because I love her so.

She always is harmonic,
She never flirts or winks;
And though she takes a tonic,
She never eats or drinks.
Her stomjack's always empty but
She never seems to care,
While she can get some scrapings, she
Will live upon the air.
She'll answer ev'ry question—
She'll instantly reply;
And at the least suggestion,
She'll laugh or she will cry.
She'll grunt or groan, and sigh or moan,
As I wish her to do
And best of all, won't speak at all,
Unless she's spoken to.

CHORUS:
So, ladies, there's a wonder,
Wonderful but true—
A damsel who won't speak at all,
Unless she's spoken to.

Note: Chance Newton, for the third line of the first
verse and the third chorus records: "I take her by the
waist like that." A "cadenza" followed the tenth line of
each verse, and, after the last chorus, Chirgwin yodeled.

My Fiddle Was My Sweetheart

Sung by G. H. Chirgwin, and composed by him; Written
by Charles Osborne; Arranged by H. Simpson. Copyright:
Bowerman & Co.

Andante moderato

My fid - dle was my sweet-heart, but now that's not the case, I've

found, you know, an - oth - er "beau," who bet - ter fills her place; In -

fact I've struck a fi - ner chord, that would not let me rest, Al -

though it did seem fun - ny, I "son - a - ta" found 'twas best; His
(sym - pho - ny,)

mu - sic is far sweet - er than a - ny vi - o - lin, Al-

though a "nat-'ral" crea-ture he's "sharp" when he be-gins; His "neck" is sim-ply per-fect, to his charms I'm wide a-wake, He's tight-ened up my heart-"strings," I fear they ne'er will break. My fid-dle was my sweet-heart, But she's a bro-ken toy, In-stead of her, I far pre-fer my lit-tle ba-by boy.

My fiddle was my sweetheart, but now that's not the case,
I've found, you know, another *"beau,"* who better fills her place;
In fact I've struck a finer chord, that would not let me rest,
Although it did seem funny (*Symphony*), I *"sonata"* found 'twas best;
His music is far sweeter than any violin,
Although a *"nat'ral"* creature, he's *sharp* when he begins;
His *"neck"* is simply perfect, to his charms I'm wide awake,
He's tightened up my heart *"strings,"* I fear they ne'er will break.

CHORUS:
My fiddle was my sweetheart,
But she's a broken toy,
Instead of her, I far prefer
My little baby boy.

Although it did seem "double bass" for me to change my tune
If I inclined to change my mind, I thought t'would best "bassoon."
I wouldn't "harp" upon the theme to my deserted pet,
I meant that day to "guitar" way before she "cast-a-net."
My matrimonial "organ" will play without a "stop";
He "pegs" away till often my ear—"drums" seem to pop.
He'll not play "2nd fiddle" to the highest in the land,
But stamp and tease to show that he's the "leader" of the band.

Few performers can be less adequately represented by the songs he made phenomenally famous than Chirgwin by "The Blind Boy" or "My Fiddle Is My Sweetheart." These two songs are not only rightly closely associated with his name, but they remained extraordinarily popular with music-hall audiences. No performance by Chirgwin was possible without one or both songs. This, and the curious garb he adopted, may make him seem an exceptionally monotonous artiste. Yet it is evident from the many accounts of him, and even from what is inevitably a travesty of his act on an old pre-1914 Edison Bell cylinder, "Some Eccentric Gaglets," that he combined with this fundamental make-up and basic repetoire, a highly varied act, and the gift of making even the most familiar aspect of his act seem spontaneous. Although Harry Reynolds has an illustration of him in his *Minstrel Memories* in mock Highland dress, Chirgwin normally made up with burnt cork; and, following an occasion when he had accidentally rubbed away a portion of the black over his left eye to reveal the flesh beneath, much to the audience's amusement, he always left a diamond of white over that eye. Yet he was able to make his inevitable appearance in this fashion seem spontaneous. Macqueen-Pope describes how he made his entrance with the eye obscured by the rim of a very tall, slender hat, and then:

> At the right moment he would jerk the hat back—and
> there was the eye, and the roar of laughter. The hat
> never fell off, a tuft of hair sprang from his head and
> saved it; and those who had seen it happen hundreds
> of times always welcomed it again and again.

With this gift of investing spontaneity in such a contrived act (and the device Macqueen-Pope describes is itself as liable to become time-worn as the eye patch) went a gift for getting on well with the audience. In the act itself the audience never knew what would happen next—except that at the end would come one or both of the favourite songs.

Chirgwin played a variety of musical instruments, some of his own eccentric devising; he danced, he punned atrociously (he said of his billing as the "White-Eyed Kaffir," according to Chance Newton, that "he didn't Kaffir it"), made topical comments, and sang in a rich baritone and in a shrill but exceedingly powerful falsetto that must have taxed the Edison Bell resources to their utmost. Chirgwin turned from one kind of act to another very rapidly, giving but a snatch of song or a seemingly impromptu verse before turning to a moment's dancing, to yodeling, to a sentence or two of repartee, and then back to another snatch of song. At the end of his act he would ask in response to the shouted requests whether it was to be "The Blind Boy" (a pathetic ballad written by one of the cornermen of Christy's Minstrels, Pony Moore) or "My Fiddle Is My Sweetheart." Both songs derived from his minstrel period and "My Fiddle" was written by Harry Hunter, one-time Interlocutor of the Mohawk Minstrels and later one of the founding members of the great music publishing house, Francis, Day & Hunter.

I don't think anyone could claim any great quality in these songs. Their phenomenal success was due to Chirgwin's personality, the peculiar power of his falsetto, and to the insistent delight that English audiences take in the pun—especially the bad pun. It is curious how strong a hold the thoroughly bad pun has over English audiences. It can't be reconciled with any theory of literary quality, but it is as prevalent in England to this day (as in a radio programme with a fairly large following such as *Round the Horne*) as it was in Shakespeare's time. It is possible to explain in a scholarly fashion the "serious" punning in *Richard II* as the intensification of language as a means of expressing intensified emotion (in Act III, Scene iv, for example, when the Queen is in the garden), although this is not wholly satisfactory. It is very much less satisfactory as an explanation of Gaunt's punning on his name which draws from King Richard the question, "Can sick men play so nicely with their names?" (Act II, scene i), or, to go even further back in time, to the punning by Sophocles on the name of Ajax in a similar fashion.

Nowadays we don't quite know how to take this mixture of the grave and the comic, and literary criticism is floored by the bad pun. The puns in *Richard II* are chiefly serious; they never sink to the depths that Chirgwin's do, but can this be said of those in, say, Act III, Scene ii of *The Comedy of Errors* (not to speak of non-Shakespearean drama)?

I confess that the bad pun, in the right context, gives me perverse delight, although I am not particularly happy about those in these two songs. Nevertheless they are in accord with the fearful punning of Chirgwin's act, and indeed they are part of a much wider popular dramatic tradition that is still very vigorous. Perhaps this delight in the bad ought to be deplored on aesthetic grounds, and doubtless it makes some sort of comment on the English sensibility, but it is most certainly a firm part of the English comic tradition. It may be that it springs from a sense of rebelliousness against established norms—a form of rejection of Establishment itself.

In presenting "My Fiddle Is My Sweetheart," I have given the current version published by Francis, Day & Hunter but have included a variant recalled by Chance Newton. Notice that 'rosin' and its pun, reason, are both sung. In the companion song (also given here) an even more ferocious series of puns occurs. It is printed exactly as it was some sixty years ago so that the full "quality" of these puns might be appreciated, in particular the way in which attention was drawn to them.

Chirgwin had a large variety of songs, including, understandably in view of his make-up, a number of the then-popular "coon" songs: "The Rag-time Coon" and "The Would-Be Coon," for example. He had a number of Cockney songs, including "The Cockney Linnets," and several which were a cross between both kinds—Cockney—"coon" songs: "The Cockney Coon's Sweetheart" and "The Cockney Piccaninnies Serenade." He even had a Scottish song, "All Scotch."

The relationship between Cockney London and the Deep South may seem rather remote, but, as Chirgwin sang, "They're quite as black as the coons down East, Our Cockney Piccaninnies." The compass direction is quite correct; it is the punctuation and expression that make it seem that West or South should be used instead of East; "Our Cockney Piccaninnies in the East End of London are as black as any coon—because they are so grubby."

You've Got A Long Way To Go

Sung by Frank Coyne. Written and Composed by A. J.
Mills and F. W. Carter. Copyright: Francis, Day &
Hunter, Ltd.

One morn-ing in a lit-tle tail-or's shop I saw displayed ___ A pair of la-dies' bloom-ers, seven and
six-pence, rea-dy made; ___ I took my daugh-ter
in next day, the fel-low got his tape, ___ And
mur-mured as he start-ed put-ting it a-round her shape: ___
Chorus:*
"You've got a long way to go, ___ you've got a long way to
go; ___ Oh! what a ter-ri-ble lump of stuff, The

124

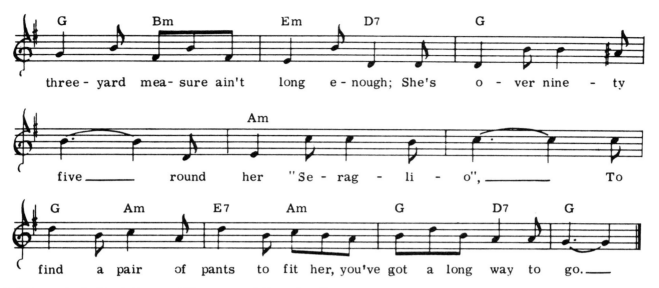

three - yard mea- sure ain't long e - nough; She's o - ver nine - ty

five _____ round her "Se - rag - li - o", _____ To

find a pair of pants to fit her, you've got a long way to go.___

*Repeated, first time softly, second time loudly.

One morning in a little tailor's shop I saw
A pair of ladies' bloomers, seven and sixpence, ready made;
I took my daughter in next day, the fellow got his tape,
And murmured as he started putting it around her shape:

CHORUS:
"You've got a long way to go, you've got a long way to go;
Oh what a terrible lump of stuff,
The three-yard measure ain't large enough;
She's over ninety-five round her "Seraglio,"
To find a pair of pants to fit her, you've got a long way to go."

Once on a donkey's back, I tried Dick Turpin's ride to York,
When suddenly the moke stopped dead and I got off to walk.
'Twas miles out in the country and he wouldn't move for me,
I asked a slop where London was, "Lord luv a duck," said he:

CHORUS:
"You've got a long way to go, you've got a long way to go."
He gave the Jerusalem moke a smack,
And planted a pin in its "Union Jack,"
He wouldn't move an inch, the copper said, "What ho!
You'd better get hold of the donkey's rudder, you've got a long way to go."

My wife ain't noted for her looks, her chivvy chase, Oh lor!
It's like a Chinese puzzle or the knocker on the door.
The kids all called her "Monkey Brand" in our locali*tee*,
To find out such a specimen of phi-si-og-no-*mee*—

125

CHORUS:
You've got a long way to go, you've got a long way to;
Talk of the girls at the Sandwich Isles
With warts and pimples all round their dials,
I've seen some ugly mugs on view at Barnum's Show,
But to find a face like my old woman's, you've got a long way to go.

One day I saw a lady friend a-marching up the West
With such a goody, pious band in blue and scarlet dressed;
She banged upon the tambourine, and shouted to the lot,
"We're marching on to glory!", I said, "Marching on to *What*?"

CHORUS:
You've got a long way to go, you've got a long way to go;
It's no use banging your blooming drum,
And shouting "Sinners, Oh! will you come!"
I like to hear you say you're going to glory, Flo,
If you're only as far as Piccadilly, you've got a long way to go.

You've Got A Long Way To Go is one of a large number of music-hall songs of no very great distinction that presents a different situation in each verse and gets such unity as it has by leading up to a chorus-line common to each situation. Perhaps the most inconsequential of all these songs is George Lashwood's "Fol-the-rol-lol," in which each verse is a limerick; the possibilities were endless, of course. Francis, Day & Hunter's printed version is quite different, except for the first verse that sets the scene, from the five-inch Zonophone record by an unnamed artist (but possibly Lashwood himself) made about 1900 (Number 0-42010). Such songs are virtually jokes set to music, and it is important that there should be a careful build-up to the refrain if the audience is to complete the sense and thus enjoy its participation to the fullest. In this, Frank Coyne's song is as good, if not better, than most of its kind.

The lines run on well, there is an absence of too much padding, and each situation is clearly and economically set forth. The subjects are well varied and give a cross-section of the kind of topics that seemed natural for a ready laugh in the music hall of those days: bloomers (still in this emancipated age a ready source of laughter), donkeys (and notice that the "moke" is referred to as a "Jerusalem," as in Chevalier's song), the wife's ugly face (given in rhyming slang), and the Salvation Army. The song dates from about the time of George Bernard Shaw's *Major Barbara*.

The chorus is varied on each occasion to carry on the "story" of the verse, and, as with many music-hall songs, it is repeated each time; the first time it is sung fairly softly, but then loudly.

The humour is simple. In the first two verses it depends on situation; in the third, delight in the ugly; and, in the last verse, deflation. Delight in the ugly is a common characteristic of the music hall, although the reason is not that given by Max Beerbohm: that "The aim of the Music Hall is, in fact, to cheer the lower classes up by showing them a life uglier and more sordid than their own." The devices are also obvious: rhyming slang with its consequent incongruity—"chivvy chase" and "Union Jack" (back), the quite delightful "Seraglio" for the fat daughter's posterior, the deliberately forced rhymes of "locali*tee*" and "phisiogno*mee*," with the rhyme italicised to make it more obviously forced and the silent "g" of the second word pronounced. Possibly this kind of humour is a simple kind of protest against established custom—a deliberate derivation of delight out of fully realised error or ugliness. If so it sets a suitable tone for the last verse. Ninety-five inches is considerably less than three yards, incidentally.

The last verse is the most interesting. It is not so much cynical as offering detached deflation by taking literally the metaphor used by the young Salvation Army girl. The humour is not very subtle, but there is a quite clever playing with the metaphorical "marching to glory...going to glory" (which has, in the past tense, the implication not only of triumph but also of loss—gone to pot) and the actual physical distance to be travelled from Piccadilly (in itself far removed from the glory of salvation) to the place, Glory, taking the metaphor as fact. The last verse is not one of sour cynicism but of a rather jovial, down-to-earth awareness of things as they are. It is not depressing pessimism that results from the realisation that the efforts of reformers to improve things are a waste of time, but a cheerful, amoral acceptance of things as they are. Not moral, perhaps, but not without its own kind of virtue.

I Live In Trafalgar Square

Sung by Morny Cash. Words and Music by C. W. Murphy.
Copyright: 1902, Francis, Day & Hunter, Ltd.

To - day I've been bus - y re - mov - ing _____ And I'm all of a fidg - et - y fidge; _____ My last digs were on the Em - bank - ment, _____ The third seat from Wa - ter - loo Bridge! _____ But the cook - ing and, Oh the at - tend - ance, _____ Did - n't hap - pen to suit me so well, _____ So I or - dered my man to pack up, and _____ Look out for an - oth - er ho - tel. _____ He did, and the new place is 'ex - tra', I vow! Just wait till I tell you where I'm stay - ing now:

Chorus:

I live in Trafalgar Square, With four lions to guard me. Fountains and statues all over the place, And the "Metropole" staring me right in the face I'll own it's a trifle draughty, But I look at it this way, you see, If it's good enough for Nelson, It's quite good enough for me!

Today I've been busy removing
And I'm all of a fidgety-fidge;
My last digs were on the Embankment,
The third seat from Waterloo Bridge!
But the cooking and, Oh! the attendance,
Didn't happen to suit me so well,
So I ordered my man to pack up, and
Look out for another hotel.
He did, and the new place is "extra," I vow!
Just wait till I tell you where I'm staying now:

CHORUS:
I live in Trafalgar Square
With four lions to guard me.
Fountains and statues all over the place,
And the "Metropole" staring me right in the
        face!
I'll own it's a trifle draughty,
But I look at it this way you see,
If it's good enough for Nelson,
It's quite good enough for me!

The beds ain't so soft as they might be,
Still the temp'rature's never too high!
And it's nice to see swells who are passing,
Look on you with envious eye.
And when you wake in the morning
To have a good walk for your breakfast,
And the same for your dinner and tea!
There's many a swell up in Park Lane tonight,
Who'd be glad if he only had my appetite.

When I think of those unlucky bounders,
The Morgans and Clarence de Clares,
Who are forced to put up at the "Cecil,"
My tenderest sympathy's theirs!
And to show I'm not selfish or greedy,
I just tell each aristocrat,
That I don't mind exchanging apartments,
Now, I can't say fairer than that!
But the soft-headed sillies won't hear what I
        say,
They still go on suff'ring, while I'm all O.K.

This song of the optimistic outcast is a good example of something that has occurred time and again in the history of popular song. Patriotism turned to irony and cynicism in the popular songs at the time of the Napoleonic, Boer, and First Great Wars (and at several crises in between); the sentimental was parodied; and the absurdity and hollowness of the gay but pretentious swell, ridiculed. It is, in popular song and drama (it is not a peculiarity of music hall) a very healthy sign.

Critical ridicule appears also in more sophisticated forms of entertainment. It is natural to the revue and has had an extensive airing recently on both sides of the Atlantic. There is, I think, a difference between the manifestation of this criticism in popular and more sophisticated entertainments, that is deeper than the different degrees of wit and political perception in which the best sophisticated revue (using this expression to cover a wide variety of entertainments) is very rich. Such a revue is invariably much more wholehearted in its approach. At its best it is savage, informed, and without compromise. Inevitably it causes offence and it is liable to make disastrous errors of taste (as that is generally accepted at a particular time) simply because it is pursuing a lone line wholeheartedly which conflicts with the norms assumed uncritically by society.

By contrast the kind of gentle debunking found in such a song as "I Live In Trafalgar Square" must seem thin stuff; and in a sense, it is. For that reason it can be enjoyed—it can be *taken*—by those likely to be offended by the acidity of a David Frost or Bernard Levin, while it offers very little to the politically and socially critically-conscious.

Yet, although I have deliberately compared these two forms of debunking, they are not strictly comparable. Critical revue (such as *TW3* or its successors, *Not So Much a Programme…* and *BBC 3*) is aimed outside itself, outside the world of entertainment on the whole (although there may be an occasional sketch about the B.B.C. itself, say); whereas songs such as "I Live In Trafalgar Square" or "You'll Never Be an Angel, Daddy" are directed within the world of entertainment of which they form a part and to which they are relevant. In other words I am arguing that they are part of a self-regulating mechanism which I see as persisting in popular entertainment. Although the in-humour of show business can be exasperating, this kind of self-correction can be most valuable.

Up to a point it may seem that the lack of wholeheartedness in the criticism of such songs (compared to that of sophisticated revue) is tantamount to hypocrisy, for in popular entertainment, the debunking and the debunked can exist side by side in a way which would be inadmissible in sophisticated revue. In legitimate drama this would make for fatal confusion; on the popular stage, where the *kind* of involvement (and especially the *kind* of political and social consciousness called forth as compared to serious drama) is different, this is one obvious example of the capacity for multiconscious apprehension which the popular drama fosters.

Thus, behind a song such as "I Live In Trafalgar Square," there is not only a sense of the worthlessness of the pretentious swell, but also a quality of self-supporting optimism which the basic circumstances, objectively viewed, might hardly seem to warrant. The subtitle, "The Optimistic Outcast," is most appropriate. The false values of the pretentious swell are remote from those of society as a whole, and an awareness of this caused the type to be debunked and rejected. This rejection takes a positive form in the later debunking songs by making the formerly affluent swell a tramp carrying something of the mystique of the outcast.

The balance of tones in this kind of song is now very different from the type of song from which it is derived. Where before we might accept the gay irresponsibility of the "Champagne Charlie" type, its gaiety subduing our realisation of the inherent worthlessness of the values expressed, in the "tramp-swells" we have a character cast out from society but bouyed up with an optimistic determination in the face of adversity which is at once comically incongruous and, after the fashion of George Formby Sr., admirable in its imperturbability—that most "pataphysical" of all qualities!

The ability to interpret life by inverting the normal order provides much of the humour of the song—the temperature is never too high in this *al fresco* existence and there are many in the luxury of Park Lane who would be glad of his appetite. There is pointed deflation in "My last digs were on the Embankment/The third seat from Waterloo Bridge," and this is carried through very effectively into the next lines. The humour of a good walk for breakfast, with the same for dinner and tea, is economical and telling. The chorus works well and the first two lines are a delightful interpretation of sleeping out in Trafalgar Square with the four Landseer lions "guarding" the sleeping tramp. I'm not quite certain that the last two lines aren't a little too defiant, although the mention of Nelson has been adequately prepared for. Is this defiance a little out of character with the imperturbability of the rest of the song? Perhaps there is just a hint of despair in the music which accompanies these last lines, so making an apt comment on the *assumption* of imperturbability, and, if that can be brought off, it might be argued that the song ends with a rather effective re-adjustment of values. In other words, in the last two lines, gives a sense of uncertainty, and perhaps even an undercutting poignancy to the sentiments being expressed.

Penny Whistler

Sung by Paul Mill and written by him; Composed by
George D. Fox. Copyright: Francis, Day & Hunter, Ltd.

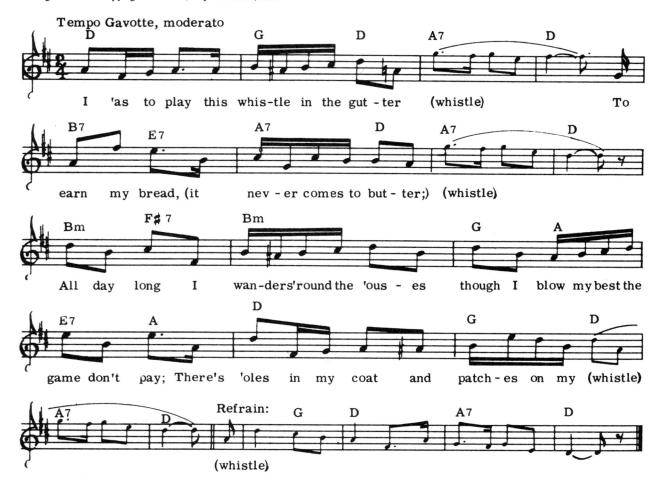

I 'as to play this whistle in the gutter (*Whistle*)
To earn my bread (it never comes to butter); (*Whistle*)
All day long I wanders round the 'ouses,
Though I blow my best the game don't pay;
There's 'oles in my coat and patches on my—(*Whistle*).

I, as a boy, got little education, (*Whistle*)
Boys *now* learn things far above their station; (*Whistle*)
With French and stuff the kids they fairly flummux;
The School Board really ought to try, instead
Of cramming their 'eads, to fill their little—(*Whistle*).

Ladies for dress 'ave always 'ad a passion—(*Whistle*)
And though they starve, they will be in the fashion; (*Whistle*)
About their togs we're always 'aving tussles,
Things called "bloomers" is the latest craze,
But one thing I've noticed, they've turned up wearing—(*Whistle*).

132

What is the good of these 'ere politicians; (*Whistle*)
They don't help us talented musicians! (*Whistle*)
When they want yer votes yer think they're tryers,
For then they say they'll give us this and that,
But it never comes off—No! They're a lot of—(*Whistle*).

I 'as a long, strong struggle for my "vittles", (*Whistle*)
For I don't come across the beer and skittles. (*Whistle*)
But in one thing we are on a level;
Parsons tell us we are all born bad
And if we doesn't alter, we're going to the—(*Whistle*).

Like "You've Got A Long Way To Go," "Penny Whistler" appears to take different and independent subject matter for each verse. It has no chorus, but there is a refrain played on a penny whistle. The refrain is taken from the morbidly nostalgic "Home Sweet Home," which also provides a couple of bars of whistling at the end of the first, second, and last lines. The last word of each verse is omitted and a cheeky piping represents the syllables of the missing words—all innocent enough: trousers, stomachs, bustles, liars, and devil. The total effect seems almost to merit one of those adjectives the desparate commentator resorts to when all inspiration fails—unusual, quaint, curious.

The choice of a penny whistle is appropriate to the song. It is the gutter instrument (I would say *par excellence* if that didn't seem an inappropriate phrase for a gutter instrument) and its thin piping can be cheeky or plaintive, making possible a measure of comment on what has just been sung.

The verses are not *quite* as random in what they have to say as at first would appear. The first is personal, describing the penny whistler's plight without a too-obtrusive self-pity. The second verse comments on boys and the kind of education they are given—and what they really need: food. Women who prefer clothes to food are the subject of the third verse, and then the penny whistler comments on the behaviour of politicians. Finally, via a return to himself, he suggests a likely fate for us all.

Thus the verses have a distinct relationship and the song as a whole makes a comment on life as it is seen from the gutter, the filling of the belly being of paramount importance. The result, especially coupled with "Home Sweet Home," ought to be depressing. There really isn't much to be cheerful about in this view of life. Yet the effect is, if not jolly, at least far from morbid. This is perhaps all the more surprising because of the use made of Sir Henry Bishop's "Home Sweet Home," a song interpolated and arranged in countless songs in the nineteenth and early twentieth centuries and written, ironically enough, as Willson Disher has pointed out, by two men who appeared to have very little inclination to find their own ways home:

> I affirm that the names associated with "Home, Sweet
> Home" (Bishop and John Howard Payne), are at best those
> of incorribible wanderers and at the worst of a downright
> homewrecker.

It was often interpolated into that other famous nostalgic ballad, "The Miner's Dream of Home," sometimes with angelic choir and chimes. Ah, those indeed *were* the days!

What saves—indeed makes—"Penny Whistler" is its sense of *gaminerie* and impudent independence. We have the feeling that someone so poverty-stricken who can so pertinently hand out such advice to those more fortunately placed, still has plenty of spirit. What is striking is not the poverty itself but the independence despite the poverty. There is, too, a nice self-deflation about "They don't help us talented musicians" and, of course, a sense of comedy about the use of the penny whistle to provide the last word of each verse. Bloomers, I suppose, must as ever provide a well-worn laugh—the kind of laugh we give to the joke of such long acquaintance that it automatically draws this response.

The refrain could be played on a penny whistle to extract the utmost plaintiveness out of "Home Sweet Home," but what seems to be more appropriate to the pathos-plus-jaunty-independence of the verses is a style of playing that undercuts the sentimentality by cheekily robbing it of its lugubriousness.

Here again is a music-hall song that juxtaposes the pathetic and the comic; furthermore this relationship is found here in a song that, though competent, tidy, and individual, is run-of-the-mill rather than great.

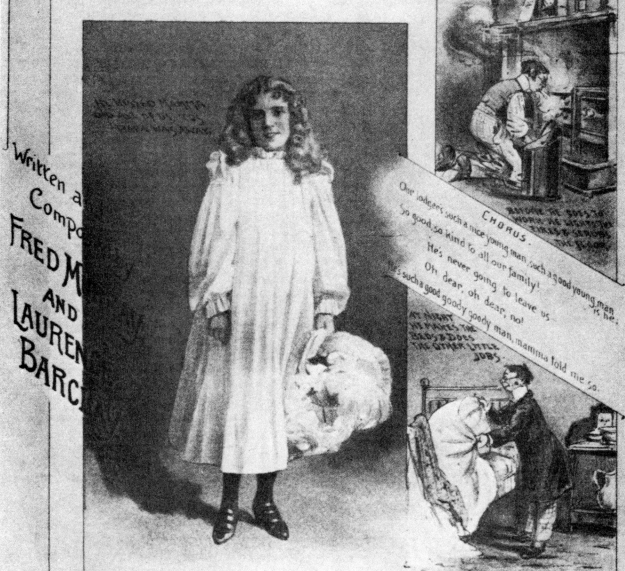

Following In Father's Footsteps

Sung by Vesta Tilley. Words and Music by E. W. Rogers.
Copyright: 1902, Francis, Day & Hunter, Ltd.

To fol - low in your fa - ther's foot - steps is a mot - to for each boy, And fol - low - ing in Fa - ther's foot - steps is a thing I much en - joy. My mo - ther caught me out one even - ing, up the West End on the spree; She said, "Where are you go - ing?" but I an - swered, "Don't ask me!" I'm fol - low - ing in fa - ther's foot - steps, I'm fol - low - ing the dear old dad. He's just in front with a fine big gal, so I thought I'd have

one as well. I don't know where he's go-ing but when he gets there I'll be glad! I'm fol-low-ing in fa-ther's foot-steps, yes, I'm fol-low-ing the dear old dad."

To follow in your father's footsteps is a motto
    for each boy,
And following in father's footsteps is a thing I
    much enjoy.
My mother caught me out one evening, up the
    West End on the spree;
She said, "Where are you going?" but I
    answered, "Don't ask *me!*"

FIRST CHORUS:
I'm following in father's footsteps, I'm
    following the dear old dad.
He's just in front with a big fine gal, so I
    thought I'd have one as well.
I don't know where he's going, but when he
    gets there, I'll be glad!
I'm following in father's footsteps, yes, I'm
    following the dear old dad.

Pa said that to the North of England he on
    bus'ness had to go,
To Charing Cross he went, and there he
    booked, I booked first class also.
I found myself that night in Paris, to the
    clergyman next door
I answered when he said, "What are you in
    this gay place for?"

SECOND CHORUS:
To follow in your father's footsteps is a motto
    for each boy,
He's trav'ling now for his firm you see, in fancy
    goods it seems to me.
My mother caught me out one evening, up the
    West End on the spree;
She said, "Where are you going?" but I
    answered, "Don't ask *me!*"

At Margate with papa I toddled out to have a
    good old swim,
I didn't know the proper place to bathe, so I
    left it all to him.
I found myself amongst some ladies, and
    enjoyed it; so did pa!
Till ma yelled, "Percy, fie for shame!" Said I,
    "It's alright ma!"

THIRD CHORUS:
To follow in your father's footsteps is a motto
    for each boy,
He just out there with fair Miss Jupp to show
    me how to hold girls up.
I'm going to hold her next, ma, but when he
    drops her I'll be glad.
She said, "Where are you going?" but I
    answered, "Don't ask *me!*"

To dinner up in town last night I went, and
    pa went there as well,
How many "lemonades" we had—my word!
    I really couldn't tell.
At tow a. m. pa started off for home, like *this,*
    and so did I!
Folks said, "Mind where you're going!" but I
    simply made reply—

FOURTH CHORUS:
To follow in your father's footsteps is a motto
    for each boy,
He's wobbling on the front, you see, and 'pon
    my word he's worse than me."
My mother caught me out one evening, up the
    West End on the spree;
She said, "Where are you going?" but I
    answered, "Don't ask *me!*"

Men dressed as women and women dressed as men were not only to be found in pantomine (see "At My Time of Life"). Barbette's act at the Alhambra in Paris in the 1920s has already been mentioned, and there were a few other men who presented an act dressed as women, of whom perhaps the best-known was Malcolm Scott as "The Woman Who Knows" (Macqueen Pope has an illustration of Scott in *The Melodies Linger On*). Many comedians have had acts in which they dressed as women, but it is the long line of women who have given male impersonations (in life as well as in the theatre, I suppose) which provides most of the highlights of such reversals. The men nearly always dress up as awkward, ugly and even deformed women; Malcolm Scott and van der Clyde were, in their different ways, exceptional, and so was Leopoldo Fregoli, who performed a series of "Quick-Change and Character Impersonations" which included an elegant woman, at another Alhambra, that in London, twenty-six years before van der Clyde's act. And there have been more recent impersonations of elegant women, including Danny la Rue and another striptease artist, Terry Durham. It is, however, the Ugly Sisters of pantomime who are closer to the common practice.

The women nearly always present a picture of trim elegance, the most obvious exception being the run-down rake, although even there an elegance of manner is usually discernible. The list is a lengthy one, and it would include Bessie Bonehill (who favoured patriotic songs), Bessie Wentworth, Hetty King, Ella Shields, May Henderson, and a host of principal boys—Florrie Forde and particularly Ella Retford and Dorothy Ward, and even a peer's wife (for in 1890 Belle Bilton was principal boy at Drury Lane under her married name, Viscountess Dunlo). It is a curious tradition and extraordinarily strong in popular drama. A short, *Pictorial History of the Art of Female Impersonation* has recently been published.

It is necessary to go back to Shakespearean and Jacobean drama to find a long run of "women" dressed as men—Rosalind, Viola, Imogen, Bellario, for example—and there special conditions operated, for the "women" were played by boy actors: in other words the reversal was a double one; sometimes the audiences knew, sometimes the second reversal was concealed from them. In the legitimate drama the part of Hamlet has always had an attraction for women (as well as comedians): Miss Marriott (whose grandson, Marriott Edgar, became a variety artist writing mock historic sketches and some of Stanley Holloway's monologues, including "The Lion and Albert"), Sarah Bernhardt, Mrs. Bandmann-Palmer (who played the part nearly a thousand times), and Clare Howard (whom Chance Newton called a "pizzicato Hamlet" because she used so much music in her production, making it truly "melodramatic") are four of the seven female Hamlets seen and discussed by Newton in *Cues and Curtain Calls*.

But of all these performers, probably the most famous is Vesta Tilley. The polish and attention to detail of her performance became a byword. Her career began in 1865 when, still a little tot dressed even then as "a man," she performed in a benefit for her father, who was a music-hall chairman at Gloucester at the time. She continued until the year after her husband, Walter de Freece, M.P., was knighted in 1919. Tilley was really her first name, it being taken as a surname after her first appearance in London in 1878. Vesta implied her brightness, after the vesta match (compare Jenny Hill, the Vital Spark). At the age of eighteen she was appearing in a Drury Lane pantomine—in male attire.

A host of successful songs have been associated with Vesta Tilley—"Algy, the Piccadilly Johnny," "Jolly Good Luck to the Girl Who Loves a Soldier" (1905), "The Army of Today's Alright" (because, with a nice touch of boastful irony in a jingoistic song, "I Joined the Army Yesterday"), "By the Sad Sea Waves" and "Following in Father's Footsteps." This last song was composed at the turn of the century by E. W. Rogers, who also wrote "When A Fellah has

Turned Sixteen," "The Midnight Son" and "It's Part of a P'liceman's Duty" for Vesta Tilley, as well as Alec Hurley's "Lambeth Walk", mentioned elsewhere.

"Following in Father's Footsteps," besides being very popular in its time, is a good example of the kind of a song that Vesta Tilley did well. The song, *projected well*, has sparkle and liveliness. The choruses are varied and each goes well with its verse. It allows, too, for plenty of business appropriate to a smartly-stepping male impersonator.

I cannot help feeling, however, that its attitude is basically the same as that of "Champagne Charlie". Possibly what makes it a little more acceptable is the impersonation which draws attention to the unreality, for this kind of impersonation was skillfully ambivalent. The imitation of the male was as exact and convincing as the artiste could make it, but the essential femininity of the performer was nevertheless subtly and often intriguingly apparent. Thus the knowingness that goes with such a line as "How many 'lemonades' we had—My word! I really couldn't tell" is not only made innocent of the leer that might otherwise lurk therein but, through irony, such knowingness is gently ridiculed. But is the ridicule too gentle? Is there in the song an affectation of innocence? Is the adopted pose of youthful raffishness cheeky enough? I'm inclined to think (although performance might well affect this judgement) that the song falls between the two stools of genuine innocence and thoroughgoing roguery. It is this lack of certainty that makes this, and so many of the songs of the male impersonators, less enjoyable and less worthwhile than their reputation might lead one to expect. There are exceptions, and Ella Shields's "Burlington Bertie from Bow" would be one.

But this is to be a little hard on Vesta Tilley. She did seem conscious of the inadequacy of the kind of world she was portraying and, as Christopher Pulling has pointed out, like the Lions Comique before her she began the process of debunking. She was not alone in this, and it is to be found in two songs by men also given in this volume, Morny Cash's "I Live in Trafalgar Square" and George Formby Sr.'s "We All Go Home in a Cab."

It may seem that what is being said is that nowadays we (Or at least I) appreciate a song that has about it irony and deflation. In part this is true: irony and deflation have an appeal now. But this is not the whole story. Through irony and deflation, songs such as "Burlington Bertie", "Waiting at the Church" or "Jeerusalem's Dead!" reveal a conflict of tones which enables them to analyse in a modest way the little world they are concerned with. Songs such as "Champagne Charlie" evoke a now meaningless dream-world, and even where this is modified, as in "Following in Father's Footsteps," the total result is nebulous. Although the dream-world is distanced sufficiently for its sense of hollowness to be conveyed, the result is unsatisfactory, partly because the exposure is not thorough enough, and partly because no positive, fully-grounded attitude replaces it. It is as if the inadequacy of the dream-world had become subconsciously apparent but has only vaguely been realized. In this respect, "I Live in Trafalgar Square" is just that much more adequate. What at the time made these songs such a success was the personality of those like Vesta Tilley who performed them (although there were few quite "like" Vesta Tilley).

Waiting at the Church

Sung by Vesta Victoria. Words by Fred W. Leigh; Music
by Henry E. Pether. Copyright: 1906, Francis, Day &
Hunter, Ltd.

Allegro moderato

I'm in a nice bit of trou-ble, I con-fess

Some-bod-y with me has had a game. I should by now be a

proud and hap-py bride, But I've still got to keep my sin-gle name.

I was pro-posed to by O-ba-di-ah Binks

In a ve-ry gen-tle man-ly way; Lent him all my mon-ey so that

he could buy a home, And punc-tual-ly at twelve o'clock to-day

Chorus:

There was I, wait-ing at the church, wait-ing at the church,

wait-ing at the church. When I found he'd left me in the lurch,

Lor', how it did up-set me All at once he sent me round a note, Here's the ve-ry note, This is what he wrote: "Can't get a-way to mar-ry you to-day, My wife, won't let me."

I'm in a nice bit of trouble, I confess;
Somebody with me has had a game.
I should by now be a proud and happy bride,
But I've still got to keep my single name.
I was proposed to by Obadiah Binks
In a very gentlemanly way;
Lent him all my money so that he could buy a
   home,
And punctually at twelve o'clock to-day—

CHORUS:
There was I, waiting at the church,
   Waiting at the church,
   Waiting at the church;
When I found he'd left me in the lurch,
Lor, how it did upset me!
All at once, he sent me round a note—
Here's the very note,
This is what he wrote:
"Can't get away to marry you today,
My wife, won't let me!"

Lor, what a fuss Obadiah made of me
When he used to take me in the park!
He used to squeeze me till I was black and blue,
When he kissed me he used to leave a mark.
Each time he met me he treated me to port,
Took me now and then to see the play;
Understand me rightly, when I say he treated me,
It wasn't *him* but *me* that used to pay.

Just think how disappointed I must feel,
I'll be off me crumpet very soon.
I've lost my husband—the one I never had!
And I dreamed so about the honeymoon.
I'm looking out for another Obadiah,
I've already bought the wedding ring,
There's all my little fal-the-riddles packed up in
   my box—
Yes, absolutely two of ev'rything.

Vesta Victoria

Any selection of the half-dozen music-hall songs that were good in their own day and still have the power to entertain would, I imagine, include Vesta Victoria's "Waiting at the Church." A recent recording by Hattie Jacques for the Late Joys, though a trifle over-boisterous, gives a very good impression not only of the song's vitality but also of the kind of seemingly impromptu patter that often came between verses in actual performances. The song is performed before an audience and Miss Jacques effectively breaks the continuity of her performance. After the second line in the first verse, "Somebody with me has had a game," the accompanist has three chords to play marked *sforzando* while the singer pauses. Miss Jacques's accompanist plays a run in the bass with considerable vigour at this point. Turning to him she steps out of the persona of a bride left waiting at the church and complains: "I hope we're not going to have too much of that sort of thing!" And between the verses there is comic-pathetic patter.

Vesta Victoria was often unfortunate in her marital affairs in her songs. On another occasion her "mother" caught her young man's eye, and he, instead of marrying the daughter, married the mother—"And now we have to call him father." When she did succeed in getting a man to the altar, she was soon widowed and was left hoping her chilly husband had found "a nice warm fire" in the after world ("He was a good, kind husband").

"Waiting at the Church" skillfully combines comedy and pathos. There is something particularly pathetic about a bride deserted at the church, and however much the comic aspects are stressed, these do not quite completely counteract the wretchedness that underlies the situation. Comic effect is achieved in a variety of ways—by innuendo (in the first two lines of the first and third verses), by incongruity (Obadiah Binks as a much-to-be-desired bridegroom), by reversal (as in the final line of the second verse and especially in the last line of the chorus), and by the character's persistent self-deflation. Yet it is in the deflation of the bride-that-was-to-be (central to the situation of the song) that the non-comic element is particularly strong. Finally, the pathetic picture of the deserted bride is deliberately overdrawn so that the comic exaggeration parodies the pathos inherent in the subject.

It would be very easy to present the picture of the deserted bride sentimentally, but here, as in Harry Clifton's "Weepin' Willer" referred to earlier, comedy undercuts the sentimentality. Although the comic presentation of the pathetic makes it possible for us still to be able to enjoy this song, longevity is not the only result of this juxtaposition. What is even more important and, in the long run, likely to give the song sustained life, is that this comic-pathetic relationship accurately expresses a complex natural attitude: the duality inherent in such a relationship. (Compare the comic and tragic duality of jealousy.) Furthermore, it is not a third party that invites us to be amused at this pathetic sight, but the principal sufferer. The character reveals her own folly in trusting such a man, exposes herself to ridicule for being so taken in, but simultaneously reveals the pathetic desparation with which she longs for marriage.

The only weakness in "Waiting at the Church" is in the use of the chorus. This is perfectly apt for the first verse, but is less suitable for the second verse and relatively inappropriate after the third verse.

It's Alright in the Summertime

Sung by Vesta Victoria. Words and Music by Fred Murray
and George Everard. Copyright: 1904, Francis, Day &
Hunter, Ltd.

Allegro moderato

My old man is a ve-ry fun-ny chap, He's an ar-tist in the Royal A-

cad-e-my. He paints pic-tures from morn-ing un-til night

paints 'em with his left hand, Paints 'em with his right. All his sub - jects,

take the tip from me, Are ve-ry, ve-ry "Eve and Ad-am-y," And

I'm the mod-el that has to pose For his pic-tures ev-'ry day. And it's

al - right in the sum-mer-time, In the sum-mer-time it's

love - ly! While my old man's paint-ing hard, I'm pos-ing in the

144

old back yard. But oh, oh! In the win-ter-time It's an-

oth-er thing, you know, With a lit-tle red nose, And

ver-y lit-tle clothes, And the storm-y winds do blow, oh, oh! And it's blow.

My old man is a very funny chap.
He's an artist in the Royal Academy.
He paints pictures from morning until night,
Paints 'em with his left hand, paints 'em with
    his right.
All his subjects, take the tip from me,
Are very, very "Eve and Adamy",
And I'm the model that has to pose
For his pictures ev'ry day.

CHORUS:
And it's alright in the summertime,
In the summertime it's lovely!
While my old man's painting hard,
I'm posing in the old backyard.
But oh, oh!
In the wintertime
It's another thing, you know,
With a little red nose,
And very little clothes,
And the stormy winds do blow, oh, oh!

One day I am a Cupid with a dart,
And another day a fairy beautiful.
I pose as Venus arising from the sea,
In the water-butt with the water to my knee.
Then he hangs me out upon the line,
You see, I have to be so dutiful.
As I hang there, oh, he paints me as
An angel in the sky.

My old man, oh, he plays a funny game,
And I've only just begun to tumble him;
All day long he's a running out of paint,
But the paint is whiskey, don't you think it
    ain't!
These are all the clothes I've got to wear,
But I've made up my mind to humble him;
I'll take a walk up the West one day,
Just dressed up as I am.

Vesta Victoria

Apart from that lodger whom she found to be such a nice young man (but of whom we cannot but feel a trifle suspicious), Vesta Victoria in her best-known songs, when not comically bewailing her misfortune in marriage, seemed to be lamenting some other misadventure that had blighted her life. Her father wouldn't buy her a dog, and her husband insisted on her posing for his "Eve and Adamy" paintings in summer and winter. The comic element is always very strong in these songs, and there is not usually the delicate balance between pathos and comedy that is to be found in the best of Gus Elen's and Albert Chevalier's songs.

In "Waiting at the Church" the very strong comic line is partly offset by reference to a situation outside that in the song. Indeed the relationship between the situation in the song (and on stage) and the conditions of life in the real world cannot be separated, and interact in a most interesting manner. While we can readily be detached from the situation as it is presented in the song (we do not really feel involved in the persona left waiting at the church), we cannot help but bring to the song an awareness of the poignancy of such a situation in the external world.

It is dangerous to mix criteria of the world of the imaginative creation and the real world, and usually I am chary of suggesting that account should be taken of what is brought to a song—or poem, or play, or novel—from the world of real experience. On the other hand the significant difference between the achievement of "Waiting at the Church" and "It's Alright in the Summertime" depends upon our taking into account the different demands made by each song on our experience outside the song.

The strength of "Waiting at the Church" lies in the tension set up between a comic representation of a kind of loss which in real life is keenly-felt. Only if the implications of the loss which is the source of the comedy are fully grasped can the density of the emotional texture of the song be adequately realised. And this implication stems largely from our experience of the real world outside the song (but assumed in the song).

It may be essential therefore to bring into the criticism of a music-hall song some aspect of external experience, particularly if this can be seen as an understood premise which the song assumes for its full apprehension. Criticism of legitimate drama that confines itself to what is written on the page must inevitably

146

be partial (hence the difficulty that some "literary" critics have in adequately evaluating drama). The implications of performance must also be considered; and it is possible that this is an aspect that must be given even greater consideration in popular art than in the legitimate theatre, especially as mime, innuendo, and filling in, though obviously not restricted to popular drama, are more commonly found there than in the legitimate theatre.

The difference between "Waiting at the Church" and "It's Alright in the Summertime" may partially illustrate my proposition considering the need to take into account external experience in evaluating a music-hall song. "Waiting at the Church" is based upon the fact of desertion; from this fact implications are drawn, comic and pathetic. "It's Alright" depends upon the fact that it is cold standing naked in winter, but though an emotional response to coldness is perfectly feasible, such a reaction is not prompted by this song. Thus to both songs we bring experience of the external world. In the first this has deeply emotional implications; in the second it is no more than "cold" fact.

Although it may be necessary to give attention to external experience, the quality of the artistic creation will depend in part upon its capacity to make us draw on that experience. In "Waiting at the Church" the emphasis is placed entirely on the last-minute loss of a husband-to-be, and it is upon this frustration that the song depends. The song's treatment of this frustration is comic; a tension is set up with the non-comic implications that we bring to the song. In "It's Alright" there is a much greater diversification of interest. The discomforts of posing in winter appear only in the latter part of the chorus (and, in any case, this is hardly a circumstance that will be as familiar to the audience as is marriage). Most of the song is concerned simply with being nude, and it is this that (for an audience of the song's own day) served as a risquely comic subject. What makes "Waiting at the Church" a much better song is that it is so organized that it calls forth an awareness of the real-life poignancy (which we bring to the song) while presenting a comic interpretation of this situation; whereas "It's Alright" only offers comic incongruity.

All this must make it seem that "It's Alright" is a much poorer song than it really is, for I have concentrated on those aspects that make it inferior to "Waiting at the Church". It has, however, several good comic touches. The offhand way in which this Royal Academician "Paints 'em with his left hand, paints 'em with his right" implies more than it says about popular attitudes to painting, even allowing for the comic context. The transitions in the second verse from Cupid to Venus of the Water Butt to being hung on a line to dry and then painted as an angel in the sky, have a nice touch of incongruity.

On the other hand "You see, I have to be so dutiful" sounds like hasty padding the third verse is less than effective, and "Don't you think it ain't!" is awkward (though it could be made as an appeal to the audience). More seriously the basic premise is weak. Can we really believe that this whiskey-tippling "Royal Academician of the Eve and Adamy pictures" is going to be upset—never mind humbled—at the threat of his model-wife walking naked to the West End of London? The threat (or promise?) is, of course, designed for the audience outside the song, not for the husband within it; and as so often happens when the shock is administered across the footlights instead of being kept behind them (that is, within the song in this case, or between performers in a legitimate act), the effect is lost as times change.

"Waiting at the Church" is surely a first-rate music-hall song; "It's Alright in the Summertime" is still singable, but is no more than second-rate.

Prehistoric Man

Sung by George Robey. Written and Composed by
Richard Temple, Jr. and C. G. Cotes.
Copyright: Bowerman & Co.

I'm real - ly ver - y harm - less, no one need have an - y tears, Pre -
served in clay you know I lay, for twen - ty thou - sand years: I
live in a mu - se - um and the en - trance it is free Just
walk in at the front door if you want to call on me! And I'm on
show in the day - time, I'm off show at night, My
flint - head spear is pol - ished, and my man - ners pol - ished quite; A
pal - e - o - lith - ic, im - a - gine if you can A
most ter - ri - fic, though pa - ci - fic, pre - his - tor - ic man.

I'm really very harmless, no one need have any fears,
Preserv'd in clay you know I lay for twenty thousand years;
I live in a museum and the entrance it is free,
Just walk in at the front door if you want to call on me!

PATTER:
You see, how I came to be found in this way---I went to sleep one day in a
primeval forest. You know what a primeval forest is, don't you? Well, like
Epping Forest, only thicker. Well, our forests got so thick, they had to shut
some of them up. I suppose I must have slept about twenty thousand years---
I couldn't be sure to the minute, you see, my watch stopped before I woke
up; anyhow, somebody found me and shipped me over here to the Museum.

CHORUS:
And I'm on show in the day time, I'm off show at night.
My flint-head spear is polished, and my manners quite;
A Paleolithic, imagine if you can,
A most terrific, though pacific, Prehistoric Man.

We'd a prehistoric war once, and it was an awful bore
Although we gained the victory, we had to pay the score.
Although the people growled and said the Government was lax.
They put an extra pound of chalk upon the income tax.

PATTER:
Of course, we didn't have money in those days; they used to pay with lumps of
rock! This was a threepenny-piece in my time. So instead of paying our way
we used to weigh our pay! (What ho! A prehistoric joke.) Supposing you wan-
ted a drink in those days, you didn't go into a pub and put twopence on the
counter. You simply put your fist on the counter. If the landlord had a smal-
ler fist than you, he'd serve you. But, on the other hand, had he a larger
fist---It's marvellous how many widows there were in our village. We didn't
call each other Percy and Clarence in those days. No Christian names. For in-
stance, I was "He of the auburn hair!" With youthful indiscretion I married
"She of the tireless tongue." I furnished a lovely cave for her, draped with sea-
weed and full of "rocking" chairs---you know, more rock than chair. We lived
happily together till I found, during my absence, she had been breaking bread
with "He of the Knotted Knee." It cost me any amount of rock to keep it out
of the papers. I should think I spent the Giant's Causeway on it. Mind you, I
sympathised with Knotted Knee---he married "She of the Fearful Face." I
think he met her at a mask ball. She hadn't got a mask on, but he thought she
had, hence the error. Of course, we had pure minds in those days. That's why
we went about like this.
I was treated very badly at home until my fourteenth birthday. Then
father seemed to change toward me. I don't know if it was because I was old
enough to fetch his beer or what. I was an awful sport in my days. I won the
Stonehenge Waterloo Cup, three epochs in succession---with my stud of flying
alligators. I used to breed them myself---a sort of cross between a wet day and
a glow-worm. I used to play football for the Rockoil Ramblers. I was called
"He of the Anxious Ankle". We used to have lumps of rock for a football, and
when you'd broken ten toes at the game, you were an in-toe-national. I hadn't
been playing five minutes before I was an international. They were rough with
me. By the time the match finished I was wearing the Blackburn Rovers
colours, black and blue stripes---in bruises. We had funny ways of making love
then. Supposing two men were in love with one girl, we used to toss for her---
not with coins. Oh, no! We used to toss each other over cliffs. Of course,
the man who lost was no good to anybody.

Chorus

George Robey

Many of Robey's songs served as an introduction to his acts. One of these is this song about the prehistoric man. The version given here is from a volume of music-hall songs published some sixty years ago, but it is not complete. In his autobiography Robey refers to verse (or patter) not included here

> In the course of the ballad I proved that the British
> Parliament in the Geologic Past was perhaps even
> more rough and ready in its methods than it is today.
> For example, I showed that any M.P. who contradic-
> ted the Prime Minister was immediately biffed with
> a club.

From this summary the loss does not sound too disastrous. Nevertheless it serves to make the point that the songs as we have them, in print or in recordings, often only give a portion of the whole song or act. Recordings often differ from printed texts. A pre-1914 recording of "Bang Went the Chance of a Lifetime" shows not only many verbal changes, but it includes brief patter that does not appear in the printed text—and this recorded version may well be cut to suit the playing time of the record.

For "Prehistoric Man" Robey dressed himself in a shaggy doormat slung across a naked chest and wore "an auburn wig that stuck out all around my face, causing it to look like a picture of the sun at noon," as he says in his autobiography.

"Prehistoric Man" is typical of the songs used to introduce a performer in his act. It gets him on the stage and creates a certain amount of atmosphere. Even in this attenuated version, it is the patter that forms the basis of the act. As Robey commented:

> The public didn't worry very much about tunes
> so long as they heard something in the way of
> "character" or comment on life which made them
> laugh.

The patter derives its comic tension from the incongruity between the absurdly impossible and the down-to-earth realistic detail: "I suppose I must have slept about twenty thousand years"—modest laugh at impossibility—"I couldn't be sure to the minute"—bigger laugh derived from incongruity—"You see, my watch stopped before I woke up"—much bigger laugh, not because of subtlety of wit of further realistic incongruity, but because it is launched from the related laughs that have gone before.

Into this basic relationship other comic devices are worked: innuendo ("prime-evil," easily imagined in the depths of Epping Forest), reversal ("pay our way" becoming "weigh our pay," a deliberately flat joke serving as the basis for comically breaking the continuity by appealing to the audience as critic—"What ho! A prehistoric joke"), and, of course, outrageous puns.

From the printed evidence it must seem surprising that this was such a successful act. It smacks very much of watered down Gilbert and Sullivan. Obviously Robey's personality and sense of timing had much to do with the act's success —and doubtless the prehistoric had then a kind of novelty for audiences of the time. Nevertheless not every music-hall act that we know to have been successful seems quite as mundane as does this one. For us it is only the implications of such an act that can hold very much interest. Like so many songs and acts, "Prehistoric Man" reveals an enjoyment of fantasy and a playing with words that made great demands upon an audience's power to listen and actively imagine. It was the development of these capacities that made such radio shows as *Bandwaggon* of 1938 and *Itma* of the war years (and the many shows that followed them) able to rely upon an audience's capacity to pick up rapid and allusive description, situation, and fantasy very quickly.

A Thing He Had Never Done Before

Sung by George Robey. Words and Music by C. W. Murphy; Arranged by Alfred Lamont. Copyright: Ascherberg, Hopwood and Crew, Ltd.

Allegro moderato

The wind it blowed, the snow it snowed, the light-ning it did light, The
rain came down as us-u-al, and, breth-ren, well it might; For
had not dar-ling pa-pa come home so-ber that same night, A
thing he had nev-er done be-fore! It took us all our time to hold the
bull-dog Pat-sy Burke; And ma-ma tore her hair and start-ed
rav-ing like a Turk, When pa-pa calm-ly told us that he'd
been and done some work, A thing he had nev-er done be-

The wind it blowed, the snow it snowed, the lightning it did light
The rain came down as usual, and, brethren, well it might;
For had not darling papa come home sober that same night,
A thing he had never done before!
It took us all our time to hold the bulldog Patsy Burke;
And mama tore her hair and started raving like a Turk,
When papa calmly told us that he'd been and done some work,
A thing he had never done before!

CHORUS:
'Twas a thing he had never done before,
Though he'd often been to prison to be sure;
It killed our sister Ruth,
When he went and spoke the truth,
A thing he had never done before.

That very same papa was overjoyed last Sunday morn,
He'd never been so jolly since the day that I was born,
For he got his only pair of trousers out of pawn,
A thing he had never done before!
When mama saw that papa was a-treading virtue's path,
She said, Salvation Army-like, "Oh! what a soul he harth!"
She sold the clock for fourpence and then went and had a bath,
A thing she had never done before!

CHORUS:
'Twas a thing she had never done before,
Not even in the good old days of yore,
She thought she'd like a treat,
So she took on water neat,
A thing she had never done before!

When mama came home from the baths the old home went amiss;
Pa didn't recognise her so he shouted, "Who is this?"
He chucked her underneath the chin, and gave her a kiss,
A thing he had never done before!
"Ah! Harold, don't you know me? 'Tis your loving wife," she cried,
But dear papa had fainted, then to cheer him up we tried,
And as soon as he recovered, he committed suicide—
A thing he had never done before!

CHORUS:
'Twas a thing he had never done before,
To hop the twig unto another shore,
He'd a haircut and a shave,
When we laid him in his grave,
A thing we had never done before.

154

George Robey was one of the most phenomenally successful of music-hall stars. Unlike most music-hall artistes he had a middle-class upbringing. After being educated in England and Germany, he was destined first for the University of Leipzig, and then, on his father's return to England, for Cambridge. What must have seemed a catastrophe at the time eventually led him to the halls. As he tells in his life story, *Looking Back On Life,* "I was sent to Cambridge till some of my father's speculations went wrong, and I had to face the facts of life and carve out a career for myself." He began training as an engineer in Birmingham, but found that had little interest for him. He enjoyed legitimate drama, but it was a chance visit to the Westminster Aquarium that led to his becoming a music-hall performer. There he volunteered to be mesmerized by "Professor" Kennedy, and so successfully did he "perform" that thereafter he was welcomed as an unpaid "volunteer." As a result of his singing, supposedly under the influence of mesmerism, the manager of the Aquarium offered him a professional engagement, and from that moment Robey never looked back.

Robey was a talented man in and out of the theatre. He excelled as an amateur in a number of widely different fields, and in his profession he became known as the Prime Minister of Mirth and was a magnificent pantomime dame. He also played with success in Shakespeare as Falstaff (on the stage in 1935 in *Henry IV, Part I* and as the dying Falstaff in Olivier's film of *Henry V*); in comic opera (as Menelaus in Offenbach's *Helen*); and in films, including that remarkable version of *Don Quixote* directed by Pabst with Chaliapine as the Don and Robey as Sancho Panza. (He had earlier played Sancho Panza in a silent version of *Don Quixote*.) Towards the end of his long life, he was knighted.

Although he began as a singer, Robey was more noted on the halls for his acts rather than his songs. Indeed, the song most closely associated with him, "If You Were the Only Girl in the World," is not a music-hall song at all. This became enormously popular in the First Great War, following his singing of it with Violet Loraine, not in the music halls but, significantly, in revue.

Robey enjoyed playing with language in the tradition of the hyperbolic chairmen of the old halls. "Kindly temper your hilarity with a modicum of reserve," he would urge his audiences, to be followed by the blunt, deflationary, "Desist!" He would also switch from the mock-elevated to the slang in his songs. A.E. Wilson, in his biography of Robey, Prime Minister of Mirth, records this example:

> He told me my society was superfluous,
> That my presence I might well eradicate.
> From his baronial mansion he bade me exit,
> And said I might expeditiously migrate —
> In other words, "Buzz off!"

This tradition is still to be heard on radio and television in a slightly different form used by Tony Hancock and Frankie Howerd.

"A thing He Had Never Done Before" has a touch of that slightly macabre sense of humour that is frequently found in illegitimate drama. The suicide in the third verse is cleverly introduced. The reversal itself is effective—"And as soon as he recovered, he committed suicide"—and the comedy undercuts the significance of suicide. The refrain that follows is patently true, and the ensuing chorus continues the juxtaposition of macabre and comic with enough variation to avoid it being stereotyped.

The song offers a comic interpretation of the virtues of consistency. Never come home sober if you usually come home drunk. Still less, don't take a bath if that is out of character! There is a kind of implied comment in the song as well as a modest playing with words. The song reflects the kind of world in which, as J.C. Heffron sang (and as O'Casey more seriously dramatised), "We all go to work but father." Obviously this was not the state of affairs in the country as a whole, and when father did not go to work, it was often for reasons beyond his control—mass unemployment, illness, strikes, lock-outs. I wonder whether or not songs of this kind have not something of the dream-world about them. Is this how men in a very hard world would like to feel they could be—that is, men who have conquered the fear of being out of work? Is there here an element of envy of those who have shrugged off the responsibility of supporting their families? Thus must such a horrid end come to those who, as in this song, refuse Destiny's generosity!

It would be foolish to lay too much stress on the significance of the items chosen to provide the twists and turns of the song—the trousers in pawn, the Salvation Army, the clock sold for fourpence, taking a bath, and the result of kissing a wife—but what is significant is the tone in which these are presented. There is comic exaggeration (especially in the reaction to the kiss) and an obvious and not very clever guying of the Salvation Army (but notice the upper-class drawl that is imitated here), but the most common tone is matter-of-fact: pawn, bath, and clock provide, despite the song's air of fantasy, a realistic, matter-of-course background.

The refrain is reintroduced effectively on each occasion, and the expression, if not very imaginative (e.g., "And mama tore her hair and started raving like a Turk"), is, on the whole, neat—like the water. As with many of Robey's songs, such as "Without a Word," "I've Done 'Em," "Then I Understood," and "It's Hard," and two of the three given here, the chorus varies at each appearance, only a part of it being repeated throughout.

Of course, the verbal device, "the lightning it did light," isn't very brilliant, but it is evidence of a pleasure in playing with words which is to be found time after time in the popular theatre. Often the playing with words is embarrassingly puerile (especially in Chirgwin), but it has helped to keep alive an awareness of language and a delight in words that is of importance, and which the legitimate drama had not, on the whole, succeeded in doing.

Bang Went the Chance of a Lifetime

Sung by George Robey. Words and Music by Sax Rohmer.
Copyright: 1908, Francis, Day & Hunter, Ltd.

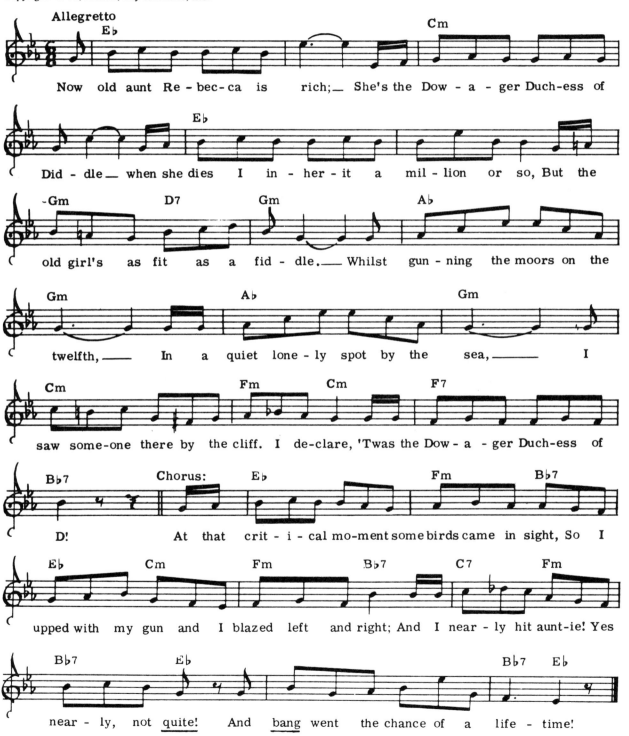

Now old aunt Re - bec - ca is rich;— She's the Dow - a - ger Duch-ess of Did - dle— when she dies I in - her - it a mil - lion or so, But the old girl's as fit as a fid - dle.— Whilst gun - ning the moors on the twelfth, —— In a quiet lone - ly spot by the sea, —— I saw some-one there by the cliff. I de-clare, 'Twas the Dow - a - ger Duch-ess of D!

Chorus:

At that crit - i - cal mo-ment some birds came in sight, So I upped with my gun and I blazed left and right; And I near - ly hit aunt-ie! Yes near - ly, not quite! And bang went the chance of a life - time!

Now old aunt Rebecca is rich;
She's the Dowager Duchess of Diddle.
When she dies I inherit a million or so,
But the old girl's as fit as a fiddle.
Whilst gunning the moors on the twelfth,
In a quiet lonely spot by the sea,
I saw someone there by the cliff, I declare,
'Twas the Dowager Duchess of D!

CHORUS:
At that critical moment some birds came in sight,
So I upped with my gun and I blazed left and right;
And I nearly hit auntie! Yes—nearly, not *quite!*
And *bang* went the chance of a lifetime.

SPOKEN: *'Twas a pity, I say, 'twas a pity, I might have
struck her with one of the pellets—however:*

Returning one night from a ball,
In a mellowish mood and reflective,
I saw a strange light in a bank—I said, "Ha!

SPOKEN: *Like that, "Ha!" (exaggerated surprise)*

I'll play Sherlock Holmes the detective."
A half-open window I spied,
And inside I proceeded to slip;
There a burglar I saw forcing wide the safe door,
So I held him in muscular grip!

CHORUS:
But he slipped and he bunked, he was wiry and thin;
And the safe was wide open and slap full of "tin"!
I drew a deep breath—then two coppers rushed in!
And *bang* went the chance of a lifetime.

SPOKEN: *'Twas a pity, I say, 'twas a pity, I might have got
some of the, er, however, Oh, I hardly like to tell you the,
er, personal, however—*

Now the wife and her mother (*Spoken:* Oh, the mother!), last June,
Went to stay with the Marquis de Caxey, (*Spoken:* She's alright, too—)
So I saw them safe off in a taxi.
At somewhere about ten o'clock
Came a telegram—Heavens alive!—
Poor dear Ma and the wife! Fearful smash! Loss of life!
Total wreck of the eight-forty-five!

CHORUS:
'Twas a terrible crash, eighty passengers slain!
And I manfully struggled my tears to restrain,
When the ghastly news reached me—they'd both missed the train!
And *bang* went the chance of a lifetime! *(Sobs)*

Once I courted a sweet winsome wench
  (Amorous sighs)
She was nineteen and also an heiress,
(It's nice when a girl is a Venus galore
And also a millionairess!)
I wooed her, I wooed, I won *(Spoken:* Wow, wow)
"My darling," she said, "I am thine!" *(Sighs)*
She swore she'd be true *(Spoken:* Get away!)
So I thought I would too;
What do *you* think? I thought it was fine!

CHORUS:
My sweet Hyacinth, fairest of flowers that blow!
(With a millionaire Pa in Chicago, what ho!)
So I put up the banns, then the wife got to know,
And *bang* went the chance of a lifetime.

Perhaps the most distinguished writer or musician to compose for a music-hall performer was Sir Granville Bantock, who, about the turn of the century under the name Graban, wrote part of the score of Marie Lloyd's "musical mixture" (to use Chance Newton's phrase—and he was the author), *The A.B.C. Girl; or Flossie the Frivolous*. Some years later he was to succeed Sir Edward Elgar as Professor of Music at the Univesrity of Birmingham. The author of "The Honeysuckle and the Bee" was a distinguished author in another field, for, according to Christopher Pulling, its author was Sol Bloom, for twelve years chairman of the Foreign Relations Committee of the United States House of Representatives (though the name appears as Alb. H. Fitz in Francis, Day & Hunter's edition). Sax Rohmer did not quite rise to such heights, but before becoming a popular novelist, he wrote songs for George Robey, of which this is the best-known.

"Bang Went the Chance of a Lifetime" has some of the characteristics of "A Thing He Had Never Done Before." The chorus varies after each verse and there is a combination of the comic and the macabre. The latter is carefully distanced, but it is there. Death comically stalks the grouse moors, and of eighty slain in verse three, alas, not poor dear mamma and the wife. The first verse is about robbery, and the last (which smacks of "Waiting at the Church") about frustrated bigamy. The comedy comes in part from the expression, but also from the basic incongruity that sees all these missed chances as so eminently desirable.

The words printed here are slightly different from those published by Francis, Day & Hunter; they come from an early recording made by George Robey. It will be noticed that there is a fair amount of spoken patter, including what can best be called "asides," even though, as in the usual music-hall fashion, the song is directed across the footlights to the audience; there is no question of the performer being "overheard" as in a legitimate drama. This form of breaking the continuity is of great interest. The audience is made momentarily aware of the performer as himself as well as of the persona that he is adopting (or the point of view that he is expressing in his song or act). This is apparent in the ooh's and aah's of relish or surprise in this song which provide, as it were, the comment of Robey the performer on the "experience" of the persona he is adopting. Comment on the act itself is very plain in the second verse in the interpolated "Like that, 'Ha!' " (*exaggerated surprise*). Sometimes the interjection is an external confirmation of what is sung within the act, as "She's alright, too," or it may not be specific, as in "Get away!"

It may seem rather portentous listing these inane comments in this manner, but this kind of double communication with an audience is a significant aspect of the music hall and it has been much practised by comedians. Max Miller and Tommy Trinder might have a pretty thin act but it was "made" by the interjections, the discussion with the audience, and the self-comment. Evidently this was Bessie Bellwood's technique. For the music-hall comedian it serves as no more than a way of extracting a laugh; and, especially at the beginning of an act, it is a good way of getting on good terms with the audience. But it makes for a very different kind of audience participation than does the kind of involvement possible in the conventional *theatre de boulevard*. The audience is constantly made aware that this is an act—that they are in a theatre—and that they are part of the whole performance. (Compare Archie Rice's line in John Osborne's *The Entertainer:* "Don't clap too hard—it's a very old building"—a favourite gag of comedians anxiously trying to jolly along an audience.) In other words the illusion of reality, so carefully built up in the "realistic" drama, is sacrificed for the sake of a laugh. What matters is not mundane similitude but imaginative fantasy. It is this, rather than attempts at realism, that is to be found in the work of the Elizabethan dramatists, and it is gradually being re-discovered now, especially in plays that, wittingly or no, make use of popular dramatic techniques. The sense of community must have been very strong in the music hall in its hey-day and it is this characteristic that cannot be recaptured for the asking.

The difference between the two approaches may be shown quite simply. A fluffed line in a legitimate play is an embarrassment. In the music hall it can get a laugh in its own right—indeed it can be so calculated to bring the house down, but not the curtain.

Thus, though the actual interjections display no wit, that they exist at all, and that this "double communication" still works, is of the greatest significance, for it is the continuation of a vital part of the dramatic heritage and it is far more im-portant than any realistic device. It is a part of the essential theatrical mystery whereby an audience is simultaneously made conscious of itself and its situation while being involved—indeed, made even to participate—in a theatrical perform-ance. It is upon this paradox that much Elizabethan and Jacobean drama depends for its full effect, and it is almost entirely due to the illegitimate drama and the capacity of its audiences that this paradox has continued to exist.

Robey, in singing "Bang Went the Chance of a Lifetime," used a very deliberate, almost clipped style, keeping each sentence of phrase distinct. One or two of the printed words make interesting comparisons with those actually sung by Robey, and these I list below by verses. The recorded version, printed here, is given first for reference:

1. saw / observed
   I upped with my gun / I lifted my gun

2. one night / one morn
   I held / I grabbed

3. Fearful / Dreadful
   manfully / painfully
   tears / sobs
   ghastly / awful

4. Once I courted / I once met
   nice / fine
   Venus galore / Genus, Milo
   also / likewise
   I wooed, I won / I wooed and I won
   My darling / my adored one
   She swore / she declared
   flowers / blossoms
   the wife / my wife.

The printed version lacks the interjections and the brief lines of patter. The vari-ations are not exciting, but on the whole suggest a slightly more polished version.

The Music-Hall Shakespeare

Sung by Emil Clare. Written by Worton David; Music by
Harry Fragson. Copyright: Francis, Day & Hunter, Ltd.

your heart. _____ And I'll hawk it round at four-

pence a pound in my ice cream cart. _____

Third Chorus:

Hal - lo, Hal - lo, Hal - lo, _____ It's a dif - fer - ent wife a -

gain. _____ With dif - fer - ent eyes, dif - fer - ent nose,

Dif - fer - ent hair, dif - fer - ent toes Hal - lo, Hal - lo, Hal -

lo _____ To me it's fair - ly plain, _____ He's

tick- led the chin of Anne Bol - eyn, It's a dif -fer- ent wife a -gain.

Shakespeare wrote a lot of plays,
Tragedies of olden days,
Wrote 'em in a manner far from gay.
Often it occurs to me,
How much brighter they would be
Written in a music-hally way.
Take "To be or not to be,"
Hamlet's famed soliloquy,
Nowadays the point it seems to miss.
But revise the tune a bit,
Put a catchy tune to it,
And Hamlet's speech would turn out more
    like this:

(To: "Let's All Go Down the Strand")
(Charles Whittle)

To be or not to be?
To be or not to be?
If I live, Ophelia I must wed,
If I die I shall be a long time dead.
To be or not to be?
I'm fairly up a tree.
If I die, where shall I go?
Even John Bull doesn't know,
To be or not to be?

Take another Shakespeare play,
Fairly brutal I'm afraid,
In which Shylock plays the leading part.
He's the Jew, of course you know,
Who from young Antonio
Claims a pound of flesh cut from the heart.
Anger flashing from his eyes—
"Curse the Christian dog," he cries,
"I will have my pound of flesh this day."
How much nicer it would seem,
If instead of tragedy
Shylock to Antonio did say:

(To: "Oh, Oh, Antonio") (Florrie Forde)

Oh, Oh, Antonio, you'll have to pay.
Though you are stoney-o,
I'll have my own-io.
I'll have my pound of flesh cut from your heart
And I'll hawk it round at fourpence a pound
      on my ice-cream cart.

Next a character I'll quote
From a play that Shakespeare wrote,
King Henry the Eighth—a wicked lot.
Half-a-dozen wives had he,
When with one he couldn't agree.
He divorced her and a fresh one got.
Till at last in righteous wrath,
Wolsey cried out, "By my troth,
This man's a libertine." Off comes his head!
But his majesty explains,
On the music halls today,
Wolsey would have simply winked and said:

*(To: "It's a Different Girl Again") (Whit
   Cunliffe)*

Hallo, Hallo, Hallo,
It's a different wife again
With different eyes, different nose,
Different hair, different toes!
Hallo, Hallo, Hallo,
To me it's fairly plain,
He's tickled the chin of Anne Boleyn,
It's a different wife again.

Parody and burlesque, especially of Shakespeare, were popular long before the first music hall opened its doors[1] and they are still to be seen. W.G. Ross, who sang "Sam Hall," was noted for his burlesques of Richard III and Macbeth. Chance Newton, in his earlier days, wrote (and played the Ghost) in a burlesque of *Hamlet,* and Macqueen-Pope quotes a verse sung by Sam Cowell at the Canterbury in the early days of music hall from his version of *Hamlet:*

> A hero's life I sing; his story shall my pen mark;
> He was not the king, but Hamlet, Prince of Denmark.
> His mammy she was young—the crown she'd set her eyes on;
> Her husband stopped her tongue, she stopped his ears with pizen.

Shakespeare (and especially *Hamlet*) has had a fascination for the popular stage. Leno, who, as Willson Disher notes, seriously wished to play Hamlet, comments on playing Shakespeare in *Hys Booke.*

> Of course, you know, I played Hamlet at Drury Lane last
> Christmas; and when I remembered that Garrick and Kean
> and a lot of other eccentric comedians had done the same
> thing in the same place, I had a sort of yearning to
> know whether they would think mine was as funny as theirs.
> Some day I'm going to tackle *Macbeth,* with Herbert
> Campbell as Lady Mac.

"The Music-Hall Shakespeare" is an "interpretation" of a soliloquy, a scene, and a character from three plays by Shakespeare (Fletcher being given no credit in the music hall for *Henry VIII*). The principal object is, clearly enough, to arouse a little simple laughter by adapting or inventing speeches akin to those in the plays, and incongruously setting them to the tunes of music-hall songs. There is not really very much more to the humour than delight in the incongruous and absurd; the situations are presented economically and swiftly and there is little padding. Two points might be suggested, perhaps with some diffidence.

The interpretations themselves are not entirely without interest. It would be foolish to take them too seriously—indeed they might better be termed *reductiones ad absurdam* than interpretations—but they do suggest how the plays struck the songwriter. The alternatives open to Hamlet are marriage to Ophelia or death; *The Merchant of Venice* is a tragedy and has as its leading part, Shylock (doubtless a reflection on the kind of performances popular at this time); and, in the case of Henry VIII, it is the number of his wives rather than the Shakespearean play that is dominant.

Secondly, it is notable in what a matter-of-fact way the music hall presents the Shakespearean issues. The tone is one of cheerful amorality. There is almost certainly unconscious irony in the second verse and chorus; hawking Antonio's heart around at fourpence a pound is hardly a "much nicer" way of expressing Shylock's demand. And, of course, there is a confusing shift in the last line; the name Antonio has suggested an ice-cream cart and it is almost as if Antonio is to hawk his own heart.

The song was written by Worton David, who also wrote (with George Arthurs) "I Want to Sing in Opera," "Hello, Hello, Who's Your Lady Friend" (with Bert Lee), and the song from which the third chorus is adapted. The music for the second of these songs and for "The Music-Hall Shakespeare" was written by Harry Fragson. Later, Worton David, like a number of other writers of music-hall songs (including Harry Hunter of Francis, Day & Hunter; Herman Darewski;

and Lawrence Wright, who wrote under the name, Horatio Nichols) went into song publishing.

Harry Fragson's fate was less happy. He is usually referred to as being Anglo-French and he worked for a number of years in Paris, including some time at the Folies Bergere. As Christopher Pulling recounts, to his father, a Belgian, Fragson spoke French, but when in England he spoke good Cockney. The father became jealous of the son (although not on this count!) and in 1913 shot him dead.

"To Be or Not to Be" is set to Charles Whittle's song, "Let's All Go Down the Strand." This was written by Harry Castling and C.W. Murphy and became very popular before the First World War. "Oh, Oh, Antonio" was sung by the Australian music-hall star Florrie Forde, who had as many famous choruses as anyone; it was written by C.W. Murphy and Dan Lipton. C.W. Murphy also had a hand, with Worton David, in the song upon which the third chorus is based, "It's a Different Girl Again." All three bear the copyright of Francis, Day & Hunter.

Emil Clare had another "literary" song. It was called "Funny Phrases," and the humour depended on taking metaphors literally—for example, to open a door with a sigh instead of by the handle. His was by no means the last of the music-hall Shakespeares. William Hargreaves, toward the end or a little after the First Great War, wrote "The Night I Appeared as Macbeth." It is in the vein of Chevalier's "The Cockney Tragedian" ("Aitches don't make artists—there ain't no 'H' in art") and it makes use of internal rhyme:

> I acted so tragic the house rose like magic
> They wished David Garrick could see.

and:

> They made me a present of Mornington Crescent,
> They threw it a brick at a time.

The play, according to Hargreaves, "though ascribed to Bill Shakespeare, To me lacked both polish and tone." Well, greater literary artists have endeavoured to improve on Shakespeare—and in all seriousness.

[1] See a good, brief account by Stanley Wells, "Shakesperian Burlesque," *Shakespeare Quarterly*, Winter, 1965.

That's the Reason Noo I Wear a Kilt

Sung and Composed by Harry Lauder; Written by him and A. B. Kendall. Copyright: 1906, Francis, Day & Hunter, Ltd.

Moderato

A lot o' peo-ple say the kilt is not the thing to wear In fact, they say the kilt is oot o' date; But I've got cer-tain rea-sons why I'm wear-in' mine, and so I'll tell ye if ye on-ly care to wait. I

used to wear a pair o' breeks be-fore I took a wife, But

af-ter I'd been wed a week or three, I sold my troo-sers, bought this kilt, the

rea-son was be-cause I'll ex-plain it if you lis-ten noo tae me:

Chorus:

Ev-e-ry night I used to hing my troo-sers up on the

back o' the bed-room door. I rue the day I

must have been a jay! I'll nev-er hing them up an-y

more; For__ the wife she used to ramble through my pooch-es When

I was fast a-sleep a-neath the quilt; In the morn-ing when I woke, I was

al-ways sto-ney broke, That's the rea-son noo I wear a kilt.

A lot o' people say the kilt is not the thing to wear
In fact, they say the kilt is oot o' date;
But I've got certain reasons why I'm wearin' mine, and so
I'll tell ye if ye only care to wait.
I used to wear a pair o' breeks before I took a wife,
But after I'd been wed a week or three,
I sold my troosers, bought this kilt, the reason was because—
I'll explain it if you listen noo tae me:

CHORUS:
Every nicht I used to hing my troosers up
On the back o' the bedroom door.
I rue the day—
I must have been a jay!
I'll never hing them up any more;
For the wife she used to ramble through my pooches
When I was fast asleep aneath the quilt;
In the morning when I woke,
I was always stoney broke—
That's the reason noo I wear a kilt.

I never would have found her oot, but one nicht I cam' hame;
I was feelin' very queer aboot the head.
I soon was in the land o' dreams but woke at three a.m.
And there she was a-standin' up in bed,
She said, "Hush, weesh! Be quiet! There's burglars! dinna mak' a fuss!
I'm feelin' in your pooches for a gun."
I don't ken if she was or not, but all I ken is this,
That there was naethin' in those pooches when she'd done.

I'm not as strong's I used to be; my blood is gettin' thin
And wouldna tak' an awfu' lot tae freeze.
The only thing I'm frightened for is winter comin' on,
I'll feel it very cauld aboot the knees.
If I should take a freezin' fit one day and kick the pail,
And join the Great Majority that's gone,
Then maybe I'll be sorry that I ever took tae kilts,
And I'll wish I'd kept ma cosy troosers on.

Harry Lauder

Most of the songs in this book are English, but the book itself is properly called *British Music-Hall Songs,* partly because the songs are part of a British heritage (although they have overstepped that boundary) and partly because the music hall was not restricted to England and many of its performers were not English. Indeed they, and their songs, not only came from all parts of Great Britain but also from abroad—especially from Australia, and also from America. One of the greatest of all music-hall performers was the Scot, Sir Harry Lauder.

Although the whole tradition of music hall can be seen as one, it showed remarkable local and national variations. Working the halls in different parts of the country required—indeed still requires—different techniques, although it is not perhaps quite as difficult as it is said to be for an English comedian to get a laugh in Glasgow. Recently the English comedian Ken Dodd described some of the basic differences in approach. In the south of England, manners comedy went well; in agricultural areas, basic life-and-death stuff; Lancashire likes the droll, dead-pan act (though Liverpool, where Dodd comes from, makes demands different from those of the rest of Lancashire); however, nothing dead-pan will go in Scotland, according to Dodd.

Lauder began his working life in a flax mill, and then worked for several years in the pits. He took to the stage singing Irish songs at first, notably "Calligan, Call again." The song tells of a pair of trousers for which Calligan the tailor is to be paid in instalments, but "since I've had them trousers, well, my work has fallen short"—and thus, when Calligan calls for his money, he gets this response:

> Said I to Calligan, "You'll have to call again."
> "Call again?" said Calligan, "Not I!"
> Said I to Calligan, "You'll have to call again,
> For I haven't got your M-O-N-E-Y!"
> Calligan vowed that he wouldn't call again,
> He swore he'd put the coppers on my track;
> Well, my temper rose, and then I said to Calligan,
> "Call again, and take your trousers back!"

Almost entirely by his own efforts, Lauder became immensely popular, very wealthy, and one of the first music-hall personalities to be knighted. Like Chevalier, Lauder wrote a large number of the many songs he sang. He was inclined in them, and also in his acts, to be overly-sentimental and was given to sermonizing.

Macqueen-Pope affectionately describes his laugh as irresistible—and from the success he was, it must have been attractive to audiences—but there is in his projection of himself on his many, many recordings, especially in this laugh, something that puts one off. Perhaps the recording conditions were to blame; perhaps I am. In the song, "Mr. John Mackie" (which he wrote himself), there is a line in the chorus that goes, "For you're the nicest chap that ever crossed the border," and, at times, and especially in his recording of the song, he seems perilously close to taking that just a little too seriously: Lauder and Mackie come very close. One could wish that in this song, and in a number of others, there was present an element of irony—or is this the misunderstanding of a Sassenach?

Nevertheless there is no gainsaying Lauder's achievement, and many of his songs have established themselves so securely that they have become a part of the "national repertoire": "Just a Wee Deoch-an-Doris," "Roamin' in the Gloamin'," "Stop Your Ticklin', Jock," "Keep Right On to the End of the Road" (a song of the First Great War in which he lost a son), "I love a Lassie," and so on and on. Each of these songs was written entirely by Lauder or with his help.

Lauder was a singer rather than a comedian, though his patter often included a rather pawky Scots humor. Although he is generally considered to be less skilful as a comedian or as a character actor than his compatriot Will Fyffe, some of his comic songs are extremely good. One of the most enjoyable is "That's the Reason Noo I Wear a Kilt," it has that element of deflation and bubble-pricking that I find lacking at times in his other songs. The story of this domestic incident plays upon the myth of the Scotsman's meanness, and it is well contrived. The spectacle of a man shivering with cold because he has adopted the national dress in order to avoid his wife going through his trouser pockets at night is very rich, particularly in the irony of resorting to the kilt, not out of national pride, but as a result of parsimony.

Nanny

Sung and Composed by Harry Lauder; Written by him
and J. H. Milligan. Copyright: 1915, Francis, Day &
Hunter, Ltd.

Moderato

I've just come here the nicht to ask you for your sym-pa-

thy, The on-ly lass I ev-er had frae me has gone a-

way. It hap-pened o'er a quar-rel that we had last Sun-day

nicht, She said I was in the wrong, but I said I was

right. My heart is near-ly bro-ken, at times I think I'll

choke When I think a-bout the prom-is-es she made.—— She

told me once sin-cere-ly that she loved me, Oh! so

dear-ly, So I've writ-ten her a let-ter and I've said:——

Come back Nanny to your Simple Sammy,
Nanny dinna say y'll leave me noo! Come back Nanny,
dinna say ye canna' For I never loved another lass but you.

I've just come here the nicht to ask you for your sympathy,
The only lass I ever had frae me has gone away.
It happened o'er a quarrel that we had last Sunday nicht,
She said I was in the wrong but I said I was right.
My heart is nearly broken; at times I think I'll choke *(Mock anguish)*

When I think about the promises she made.
She told me once sincerely, that she loved me, Oh! so dearly,
So I've written her a letter and I've said:

CHORUS:
Come back Nanny to your simple Sammy,
Nanny dinna say y'll leave me noo!
Come back Nanny, dinna say ye canna'
For I never loved another lass but you.

I really don't know what to do, I've such a burning pain,
Burning like a poultice in below my watch and chain.
I really did look forward to lead such a happy life,
But that can never be, unless she says she'll be my wife.
We used to go for long walks nearly every other night,
We used to wander doon the lover's lane
Yon was such a time of bliss, I did nothing else but kiss her,
I'll never kiss another lass again.

PATTER:
I'll do something desperate. I'll disfigure myself for life. I know what I'll do, grow a whisker and cut my hair! If I were to blame, I'd give in; but I'm not to blame. I know who's to blame. I know. It's her mother. She's the one. Mind you, a nice enough woman to look at. Oh! Quite nice. But you've got to look at her quick and then run for your life. Y'see Nanny's mother has a big family. She's got six children and three boys and it was this wee boy's birthday. That was the whole cause of it, y'see, because Nanny's mother told Nanny to write me and invite me to come down to the party. That is to the birthday party. Y'see, because there was bacon and dumplings, and oh! I can eat dumplings, I can eat dumplings with anybody. So that was the whole

cause of it. I never, I never, I never got a currant out of that dumpling. Oh, dear me! When I think about it ye know—Oh! It's her mother, that's the one that's to blame for it all. Because Nanny knows that I love her, Oh! she knows that I love her alright, and her mother knows that I love her. I'm the first sweetheart Nanny ever had, and I believe she's only doing this quarrelling to try my sincerity. And I believe she is here the nicht, listening if I'm saying anything about her. (Business: Looks round the audience, says he sees her, and sings to her:)

Chorus

Although many of Lauder's best-known songs are sentimental, he did have some of the comic-pathetic variety. For example, among the songs written about the Scot in exile, "There's a Wee Hoose on the Hillside That I haven't Seen for Years" is maudlin, but separation is seen comically in "We Parted on the Shore," with its spoonerism, "I sailed away across the maging rain," and the encouraging response:

> She asked me if I'd think of her and I said p'raps I would
> But I'd often broke my promises before.

Perhaps Lauder's most famous reversal comes in another of his own songs:

> Oh! It's nice to get up in the morning,
> But it's nicer to lie in bed.

"Nanny" is curious. It tells of a lovers' quarrel, yet the tune of the chorus is gay to the point of being triumphant. Furthermore, in his recordings of the song, Lauder deliberately overplays the tearfulness so that comic exaggeration results. The cause of the quarrel is not adequately explained, nor, alternatively, is any *lack* of an adequate cause made the point of the song. Not surprisingly, the tone of the song is confused.

The song exists in different versions. That given here is made up of the verses of the longer (HMV) recording, which conforms to the printed version, more or less. The patter is taken from a shorter recorded version with some lines missing in the recordings taken from the printed text (which has the shortest patter of all). Possibly because the humour is not strong, there are signs of reworking in each version of the patter. The opening remark and the reference to the mother-in-law's face are the only ostensibly "comic" remarks, the rest of the comedy (if such it be) being derived from the exaggeration of the pathos. There is, too, an element of "slice of life" in the patter, and we are made aware despite—or perhaps through—the pathetic exaggeration of the speaker's distress. Thus, in the patter, comic exaggeration, realism, pathos, and a couple of comic remarks follow one another swiftly, and then this patter is followed by a chorus having a completely different tone which is at variance to all that has gone before.

It is apparent from a number of the songs given here that it is possible to make transitions of this kind in the popular drama, but I don't think this is done successfully in this song. The contrasting tones are confused instead of being made into a coherent whole.

Seaweed

Sung, Written, and Composed by Fred Earle.
Copyright: Francis, Day & Hunter, Ltd.

Moderato

C ... G7
Last sum - mer time I went a - way to Dov - er by the

C
Sea ___ And thought I'd like to bring a bunch of

F G7 C
sea - weed home with me It tells you if it's

G7
going to rain or if it's going to snow ___ And

C Am D7
with it an - y - one can tell just what he wants to

Chorus:
G G C
know. With my sea - weed in my hand ___ I

F G7 C Am
got in - to the train; ___ All the pubs were closed when

D7 G7 C
I got out a - gain. I ___ could - n't get a

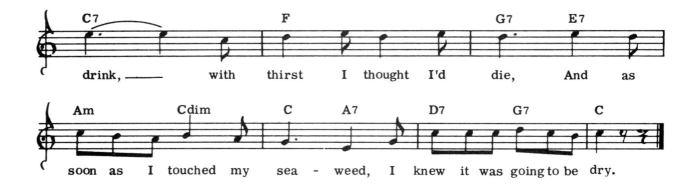

drink, ____ with thirst I thought I'd die, And as
soon as I touched my sea - weed, I knew it was going to be dry.

Last summertime I went away to Dover by the sea
And thought I'd like to bring a bunch of seaweed home with me.
It tells you if it's going to rain or if it's going to snow
And with it anyone can tell just what he wants to know.

CHORUS:
With my seaweed in my hand I got into the train;
All the pubs were closed when I got out again.
I couldn't get a drink, with thirst I thought I'd die,
And as soon as I touched my seaweed, I knew it was going to be dry.

Two lovers walked   one evening down a quiet country lane;
The chap was Honest William and the girl was Mary Jane.
They talked and walked and walked and talked about their future life;
I heard him say, "I shall be glad when you're my darling wife."

CHORUS:
Then he kissed her ruby lips and looked at her with pride,
Said, "I shall be glad when, darling, you're my bride.
Tomorrow we'll be wed and then you will be mine!"
And as soon as I touched my seaweed, I knew it was going to be fine.

I had a fright some time ago right in the dead of night;
The missus said, "Wake up you fool, the house is all alight!"
I quickly tumbled out of bed, though I could hardly stand,
My seaweed hung upon the wall, I grabbed it in my hand.

CHORUS:
And rushed upon the roof, forgot to take my clothes;
The fireman down below was squirting with his hose.
He hit me where I stood, right on the parapet,
And as soon as I touched my seaweed, I knew it was going to be wet.

One night I felt so cold in bed, I woke my wife Maria
And said, "I'm going to jump out love, and light a little fire!"
Then in my nightie I jumped out, quite balmy on the thatch,
I found the wood, and found the coal, and then I struck a match.

CHORUS:
And stood before the fire as happy as can be;
Soon I felt the warmth round my anatomie.
My shirt was all alight and I'll forget-me-not
For as soon as I touched my seaweed, I knew it was going to be hot.

In all my happy married life I'd never had a row
Till someone put the poison in and things have altered now.
My wife, when I got into bed the other Thursday night,
She put her cold feet on my back and kicked with all her might.

CHORUS:
And pushed me out of bed, I fell on to the floor;
She said she wouldn't have me back there any more.
She took the sheets and quilts, in which herself she rolled,
And as soon as I touched my seaweed, I knew it was going to be cold.

Holidays by the sea are a relatively recent development. Not so very long ago the English coast was difficult of access from most large towns and until railways (and enough money) made the journey an easy one, it was as often as not as convenient to go by boat from London to such a coastal resort as Margate some sixty-five or seventy miles away. A comic song of 1820 by Thomas Hudson, who sang at the Cyder Cellars, recounts this great adventure. The song has very lengthy patter, but the beginning sets the tone:

> A short farewell to smoke and noise,
> We're off to taste sweet Margate's joys;
> The Steam Boats wait---you'll be too late,
> If you don't make haste to th' Tower Stairs;
> See the sun sheds forth its light,
> There's not a single cloud in sight,
> While all sorts meet---in low Thames Street,
> And coaches hasten with their fares.
> Oyster dealers---fish fags---railers---
> Gentry---porters---Jews and sailors.
> All is bustle, noise and prate,
> Around sweet crowded Billingsgate.
> Eight o'clock's the time for going,
> To and fro see wherry's rowing,
> Whilst the muddy Thames is flowing.
> "Make haste coachee, pray get on,
> Hollo mate, pull up! I say,
> Your fish cart here stops up the way,
> I can't sit standing here all day,
> The Steam Boats sure will all be gone."

Billingsgate is noted as a fish market so its sweetness is open to question. The "sitting standing" concept is rather pleasant. Although they started at eight, they had not gone much past Gravesend (where they saw a fort designed to repel the *Danish* Armada) by dinner time.

As soon as the seaside became popular it replaced the river as a subject for popular songs (a transition which Christopher Pulling clearly documents in his chapters, "The Gay River" and "They Did Like to Be Beside the Seaside"). "Seaweed" is not so much about the seaside as it is inspired by it. Possibly, in these days of televised weather forecasts, the efficacy of the strand of seaweed as a weather prognosticator has been forgotten, but at one time no self-respecting family returned from a day or a week by the sea without a little bit of seaweed in order that it should know during the ensuing year whether it was going to be wet or fine, day by day.

Fred Earle, who was the son of Joseph Tabrar, the author of "He's Going to Marry Mary Ann," composed and sang this song. His seaweed was something more than a mere weather indicator. It would tell just what anyone wanted to know, and it is this capacity to forecast other eventualities than the weather which is the source of the song's humour. The result is a typical, jolly, convivial kind of music-hall song. The humour is modest, but the rhythm keeps the song moving with its alternate crotchets and quavers, and the song has a pleasant, if not very strong, air of fantasy. Although a chorus song, such are the changes made in each chorus that it is virtually a two-verse arrangement for each of the five situations. And here is a fairly obvious innuendo.

There is an early single-sided Zonophone record which has a version of this song sung by Alf Gordon. The differences between this version and that printed by Francis, Day & Hunter make a good example of the difference that exists between different versions of music-hall songs. Sometimes changes were made for copyright purposes, sometimes the changes are the result of carelessness, and often, for records, songs and acts were shortened. Thus Gordon only sings four of the five verses of "Seaweed." Nevertheless some changes suggest that performers considered they were free to adapt material to suit their own styles. It is also possible to trace the frequent slight modifications introduced into an act or song in successive recordings. Such variations discourage one from placing much reliance on any single version of a music-hall song, whether published or recorded.

In Alf Gordon's recording, the order of verses is 1, 4, 3, and 2 (5 being omitted). This was, presumably, a conscious and deliberate change. So must have been the addition after each chorus of a sequence of Ti-ity-ti-ity-ies. There are a number of minor variants in the four verses—many probably no more than degeneration through constant repetition. For example, Gordon sings "Anyone can tell just what *they* wan*t* to know"; he feels "war*m a*round his anatomy" after having lit a "*bigger* fire" and is "as happy as *could* be." In the second situation, Gordon repeats in the chorus the order of words given in the verse, whereas the printed version alters the position of "darling." William was a "man" to Gordon, not a "chap." The opening of the third verse reverses the order, Gordon singing, "Some time ago I had a fright right in the dead of night." Occasionally the change produces a better line, as in the fourth printed verse where Gordon repeats the "I" to give "I found the wood, I found the coal, and then I struck a match."

Few of these changes are of any great significance individually, particularly as music-hall songs are not noted for the precise use of language. I mention them on this occasion in such detail so that the common practice with regard to all music-hall songs can be gauged, and because they will suggest the degree of freedom with which these texts may be treated.

The Future Mrs. 'Awkins

Sung, Written, and Composed by Albert Chevalier.
Copyright: Reynolds & Co.

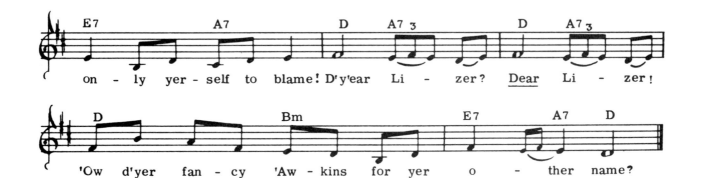

on - ly yer - self to blame! D'y'ear Li - zer? Dear Li - zer!

'Ow d'yer fan - cy 'Aw - kins for yer o - ther name?

I knows a little doner, I'm about to own 'er,
She's a goin' to marry me.
At fust she said she wouldn't, then she said she
   couldn't,
Then she whispered, "Well, I'll see."
Sez I, "Be Missis 'Awkins, Missis 'En'ry 'Awkins,
Or acrost the seas I'll roam.
So 'elp me Bob I'm crazy, Lizer you're a daisy,
Won't yer share my 'umble 'ome?"

SPOKEN OR SUNG: *"Won't yer?"*

CHORUS:
Oh! Lizer! Sweet Lizer!
If yer die an old maid you'll 'ave only yerself to
   blame!
D'y'ear Lizer?
Dear Lizer!
'Ow d'yer fance 'Awkins for yer other name?

(The last line of the third chorus runs:
Missis 'En'ry 'Awkins is a fus-class name.)

I shan't forgit our meetin', "G'arn" was 'er
   greetin'
"Just yer mind wot you're about."
'Er pretty 'ead she throws up, then she turns 'er
   nose up,
Sayin', "Let me go, I'll shout!"
"I like your style" sez Lizer, thought as I'd
   surprise 'er,
Cops 'er round the waist like this!
Sez she, "I must be dreamin', chuck it, I'll start
   screamin',"
"If yer do," sez I, "I'll kiss"—

SPOKEN OR SUNG: *"Now then!"*

She wears a artful bonnet, feathers stuck upon it,
Coverin' a fringe all curled;
She's just about the sweetest, prettiest and
   neatest
Doner in the wide, wide world!
And she'll be Missis 'Awkins, Missis 'En'ry
   'Awkins,
Got 'er for to name the day;
Settled it last Monday, so to church on Sunday,
Off we trots the donkey shay!

SPOKEN OR SUNG: *"Now then!"*

Albert Chevalier

It is among the Cockney music-hall songs that are to be found some of the best "songs from the heart" sung in the halls. Good comic songs are to be found fairly readily, but, as is discussed elsewhere, songs of love and grief are nearly always so uncontrollably expressed that, although they could be taken seriously in their own time, they seem comically exaggerated to a later generation. When sentiment, or "sincerity" is expressed within a comic tonal framework, however, deeply-felt feelings may not only still be made acceptable to us, but, in addition, a rare quality of insight and expression occasionally may be shown. Something of this has been suggested in "Cushie Butterfield" and "Waiting at the Church," although there the comic predominates. The relationship of sentiment and comedy is to be seen at its best in some of the songs of Gus Elen and Albert Chevalier.

Chevalier was not of the music hall, nor did he ever feel himself to belong there. He had been a straight actor for fourteen years from his first appearance in 1877 with the Bancrofts, and it was only as a result of a lengthy period without work that he succumbed to the persuasions of friends that he should try the halls. He feared his quiet style would be hooted off the stage, but his success was instantaneous and enormous. Chance Newton and Macqueen-Pope mention the songs he sang in his first appearance (though the lists differ slightly). They were largely of his own composition but with some of the music written by his brother, Charles Ingle. The songs chosen give an indication of the kind of programme he offered:

> "The Future Mrs. 'Awkins"
> "Knocked 'Em in the Old Kent Road"
> "Coster's Serenade"
> "Funny Without Being Vulgar"
> "The Hasty Way 'E Sez It"

Two of these are love songs (although such a definition is not quite appropriate; Chevalier often used the description, "A Cockney Carol"), two are wryly comic, and one is rowdily so.

Chevalier's association with the legitimate stage is apparent in the kind of dramatic monologues he favoured. To hear him giving his monologue, "The Fallen Star," in an old recording is to be taken back to a remarkably different style of acting where the pathos was "rendered" in the most extravagant style, with highly dramatic pauses, wide variations in pitch and volume, and an almost palpable sincerity. Indeed, when he wrote of love or affection outside a comic framework, he reveals the kind of excess that is so common in Victorian songs from the heart. Whether the story that his wife, Florrie (who was George Leybourne's daughter), inspired his song, "My Old Dutch," is apocryphal or not, it is impossible to be sure; but from the internal evidence of the song's tone—its patent, unmitigated, heart-on-sleeve sincerity—one can well believe it was a genuine tribute to his wife. This song has maintained its existence—a case of sincerity rather surprisingly winning through in a cynical world—but it lacks the complexity of tone that makes a song such as "The Future Mrs. 'Awkins" such a delight.

Chevalier's association with the world of the legitimate drama, his recitals, and especially the fact that he could never bring himself wholly to embrace the world of the halls, inevitably distanced him a little from many of his colleagues. He is that rarity in the halls before the First Great War, an outsider from the middle class. Unlike George Robey, however (another such, whose *forte* was the extravagant act), Chevalier seemed able, as few Cockney comedians were, to express and get beneath that way of life. It is true that there is an element of idealisation in the Cockney world of his songs, but at his best he is able to get to its roots in a way that is only very rarely found in any other songs of this kind.

Songs of Cockney life go back, in the music-hall period, to those made popular by the Great Vance, George Leybourne's rival. Probably the best-known of his Cockney songs was "The Chickaleary Cove," of which this is one of the more or less "elegant extracts" quoted by Chance Newton:

> I'm a Chickaleary bloke with my one—two—three—
> Vitechapel was the willage I was born in;
> To catch me on the hop,
> Or on my tibby drop,
> You must vake up wery early in the mornin'.
> I've got a rorty gal, also a knowing pal,
> And merrily together we jog on.
> And I doesn't care a flatch
> So long as I've a tach,
> Some pannum in my chest—and a tog on!

Often the colloquialisms make the songs virtually incomprehensible, becoming what Chance Newton liked to call "slanguage." Rhyming slang was often used (especially by Hyram Travers) and in some of the songs there is the same kind of energy that is to be found in Chevalier and Elen; in, for example, a chorus from Teddy Mosedale's song, "My Chestnut 'Orse," also quoted by Chance Newton:

> Like a hengine he could go
> To 'Ackney, 'Ampstead 'Eaf, or Bow,
> I never shall survive the lorse
> Of poor old Jack, my Chestnut 'Orse!

Though these songs reflect something of that vivacious attitude to life so often manifested by the Cockney, not even those of Marie Lloyd's second husband, Alec Hurley, the Coster King, revealed such sensitivity to the way of living that is to be found in Chevalier's and Elen's songs. Hurley's best-known songs were " 'Arry, 'Arry, 'Arry" and "The Lambeth Walk," though not that sung by Lupino Lane some years later. Hurley's "Lambeth Walk" goes:

> You may talk about your Cake Walk
> The Lambeth Walk, it knocks 'em all to smithereens;
> It ain't no bloomin' fake walk,
> It's the same as we do when we're out selling greens,
> For we don't want no banjos, burnt cork or any fake;
> The Lambeth Walk—there ain't no talk,
> For that Walk takes the cake.

In view of Chevalier's attitude to the halls, it is a little surprising that he is able so well to get into the world about which he sings and to show such sympathetic understanding about it. He certainly knew the world about which he sang very well from close acquaintance and possibly his songs are the result of the conflict of association and detachment.

The verse of "The Future Mrs. 'Awkins" may be spoken or sung. The music is given as composed by Chevalier himself. He did write most of his songs, though the music was usually composed by someone else, often his brother, Charles Ingle, or his accompanist, Alfred West. It is not always possible to be sure that a singer given the credit for writing a song actually wrote it. For example a Zonophone recording by George Formby, Sr. of "We All Went Home in a Cab" lists him as the composer, whereas the song was the work of Harry Wincott and George Le Brunn. Max Miller frequently joked about ghosting. Though Chevalier certainly did write his own songs, Chance Newton records that "Mrs. 'Enery 'Awkins" was provided with its "sweet melody" by John Crook, who, among other music for Chevalier, wrote the melody for "Jeerusalem's Dead!"

The chorus has an attractive lilt on the name, "Lizer," and there is an effective use of two words spoken (or sung, if the verse is spoken) before the chorus. It is easy to sentimentalise this song in performance, and though Chevalier (if his own recordings of "My Old Dutch" and "The Fallen Star" are anything to go by) may well have done so himself, I am certain that a non-sentimental interpretation, giving full weight to the touch of mockery in the song, does it most justice.

Like "Cushie Butterfield" this song makes use of a sub-language, and, again like "Cushie Butterfield," it presents courtship (this time successful) in a way that seems to spring from within the society with which it is concerned. The Cockney dialect is not employed for trivial comic effect in order to raise an easy laugh simply because of its difference from standard English—as it would be spoken by a comic, stereotyped, working-class house servant in an upper-middle-class West End play. It is used because this is a natural form of expression; and, from the first, we are made aware of the sympathetic use of dialect.

The effect of cross-dialogue, particularly in the second verse, is skilfully achieved and Chevalier, in the song's few lines, outlines clearly and strikingly the individuality of the two lovers. One characteristic of the Cockney is strongly brought out: pride in himself. This is not presented sentimentally (as in Noel Coward's "London Pride") or brashly, but through a quiet, dignified insistence upon proper names, culminating in the assurance that 'Missis 'En'ry 'Awkins is a fust-class name." 'Enry Doolittle is perennially amusing—and Shaw, and we, are sympathetic towards him. But he expresses an outsider's view of working-class Cockney morality for an audience of outsiders. We are sympathetic to 'Enery 'Awkins, but our sympathy is never requested: Hawkins is proud to be what he is, as he is; and further, Chevalier (despite his attitude to the halls) convinces us that he is presenting him from within his own experience and for an audience of Hawkins's own kind. The result is a perfect naturalness which the writing of outsiders, however gifted and observant as were Galsworthy and Kipling, and even if responsible for literature of great stature, as were Shaw and Conrad, can can never quite match.

Pride is evoked, not baldly stated, and the effective and rather unusual pun in the chorus on "D'y'ear Lizer?" and "Dear Lizer" allows for tenderness without mawkishness. The very slight touch of the comic undercuts any trace of sentimentality that might be present.

"The Future Mrs. 'Awkins" was designed to appeal to a mass audience, specifically a working-class Cockney audience. In this it was very successful. Nevertheless I believe that a more literary audience can appreciate it as an expression of the world and the tradition from which it springs. Such an audience can appreciate its observation and the instances of imagination and technical skill which are superficially apparent. But there is more to this song than noting, say, Lizer's reactions at the beginning of verse two, or the contrast of spoken and sung words.

As with "Cushie Butterfield" it is possible to bring to "The Future Mrs. 'Awkins" an awareness of the whole tradition of courtship poems, and these songs enrich and enlarge that experience. In addition, although the song is not specifically comic (it was called by Chevalier "A Cockney Carol"), it reveals a touch of that conflict of tone which is so remarkable a feature of many of the best comic music-hall songs and acts. Beneath the expressions of love and the humorous touches, there is the repeated threat of dying an old maid. In such a world this was not merely a fearful threat of sexual failure, but, much more seriously, a warning of the dangers of attempting economic independence if a single woman in this society.

In this song, complexity arises from a conflict of the tones of love, humour, and painful reality, all subtly balanced one against the other. Perhaps it is not too absurd to call this "a kind of wit." The result is a song which, within its modest scope, illuminates and analyses the life it is concerned with. Furthermore its conflict of tone makes it possible for it to appeal outside the age, and to a different audience from that which first heard it.

"Jeerusalem's" Dead!

Sung by Albert Chevalier; Written by Brian Daly; Composed by John Crook. Copyright: Reynolds & Co.

188

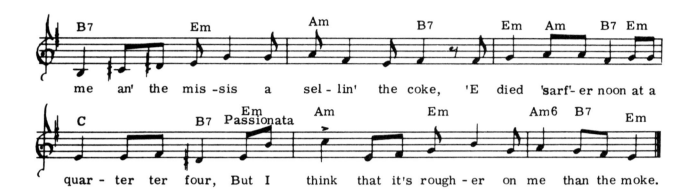

me an' the mis-sis a sel-lin' the coke, 'E died 'sarf'-er noon at a quar-ter ter four, But I think that it's rough-er on me than the moke.

I've 'ad four 'arf-pints at the *Magpie an' Stump,*
An' two goes o' rum jes ter keep up my sperrits;
My mince-pies are waterin' jes like a pump,
　An' they're red as a ferrit's.
'Cos why? 'Tain't the missis nor kids wot I've
　lost,
But one wot I careful-*lie* doctored an' fed;
The nussin' an' watchin' 'as turned out a frost,
　The Jeerusalem's dead!

CHORUS:
Yer won't see 'im pullin' the barrer no more,
Wi' me an' the missis a-sellin' the coke.
'E died 's arf'ernoon at a quarter ter four,
But I think that it's rougher on me than the
　moke.

'E 'ad a big 'eart and a strong pair o' 'eels,
A temper as short as was e'er manifactured;
In 'arness 'e used ter do 'ornpipes an' reels,
　An' my ribs 'e once fractured!
'E bit like the devil, and eat like a 'orse,
An' orfen 'e'd try ter stan' up on 'is 'ead;
It's all over now wiv 'is tricks an' 'is sauce,
　The Jeerusalem's dead!

I stroked 'is old 'ead as 'e laid in the stall,
An' some'ow or other I felt I *must kiss* 'im!
I've a wife an' some youngsters—'e wasn't
　quite all, But I *know* I shall miss 'im.
There's one thing I'm certain, 'is grub was
　the best,
An' I've gone short myself ter purvide 'im a
　bed;
Come 'an 'ave 'arf a pint—there's a lump in
　my chest
　The Jeerusalem's dead!

To pick from the wide range of songs sung by Chevalier this one and "Mrs. 'Awkins" is hardly being representative, but as both are good examples of the juxtaposition of the comic and emotional, and as these are, when successfully brought off, rarer than good comic songs, I have chosen two of a kind. Chevalier had a wide range of songs. One of several albums of his songs contains "Jeerusalem's Dead!" and "My Old Dutch"; several comic Cockney songs; the toff song, "The Johnnie's Serenade"; a mock-French song, "Tink-a-Tin"; a song of moral advice, "Yours, Etc.;" and a country yokel song, " 'E Can't Take a Roise Out of Oi," which has this final verse ("me" is 'E's 83-year old father):

'E mustn't think as 'ow becos 'e's lived i' Lunon town
'E's ev'rybody—*me* amongst the rest!
Oi've 'arf a moind to show un up, or reyther take un down.
Oi 'ardly knows which way 'ud be the best.
Soomtoimes I lets un talk, an' then Oi bursts into a laugh,
Oi never did 'ear sich a pack o' loies;
'E sez as 'ow 'e's seed a thing they calls a "fonygraph"!
You turns a 'andle an' it talks an' croies!

CHORUS:
Oi've been moindin' the farm 'ere fur forty-five years
An' afore that, the pigs in the stye,
An' Oi knows what Oi knows, an' Oi 'ears wot Oi 'ears,
An' 'e can't take a roise out of Oi!

This is not completely unsympathetic to the old man, and it shows off neatly the man proud to have travelled, in his eighty-four years ("coom Christmas"), all of twenty miles from his village; but it is not irradiated by the life which it purports to represent. It has the character of the onlooker observing, and this is to be seen in the lack of that inherent natural dignity which is to be found in Henry Hawkins and by the use of dialect simply for its comic potentialities.

Although Chevalier wrote the words to most of his songs, he did sing songs written by others, and "Jeerusalem's Dead!" is one of these. The introductory accompaniment is marked "Mournfully," but the opening sounds a little like a wry Medelssohnian Hee-Haw, and the vocal line accentuates this wry mourning, especially in the three sobbing ornaments in the penultimate line of each verse. For the chorus, the instruction *tranquillo* is apt, and all in all, the music gives not merely support but individuality to the song, having a quality of its own that corresponds to the conflict of tones in the words.

The song is a lament for a departed donkey ("Jerusalem" being a term for a donkey after the city into which Christ rode in triumph on Palm Sunday), and the loss of this donkey is serious for the coster. I stress this because so pervasive is the humour, so wry the pathos, and so frequent the deflation that it is necessary to bear in mind that the subject of the song—the death of a donkey—is a matter with serious implications for its owner.

First and foremost this song avoids completely any trace of false sentimentality. Compare it with, for example, the optional spoken finale "As rendered by Miss Vesta Tilley" after the third verse of Leslie Stuart's "Sweetheart May":

I found her the same "Sweetheart May" I had pictured
in my dreams, in lands over the sea. I gave her my
hand in the hope that she would greet me as of old. But
I was forgotten. I said, "May, don't you remember me?

Can't you recall the time when you asked me to wait till
you grew to be a woman that I might marry you, and don't
you remember the little song I used to sing you?" I sang
her the song once again, but no!, she only said, "I
cannot recall you, nor do I remember the song. Besides,
we must part—Tommorrow I am to be married—Good-bye!"
"Married! To-morrow! Oh, May! But there—God bless
you, May—Goodbye."

The false sentiment here needs no pointing out. What keeps "Jeerusalem's
Dead!" from such mawkishness is perhaps that it is not envisaged as a song of
grief for a dearly loved pet but as a lament for the loss of an essential part of
the capital investment of this rather small coke distribution organisation. This
can clearly be seen in the second verse where the donkey's assets are stated—" 'E
'ad a big 'eart and a strong pair o' 'eels"—quite flatly as if it were a first-class
piece of mechanism that is no more, not a dear, big-hearted, little trotter. It's
a damn good working beast that has been lost! And quite plainly he was not
sweet-tempered nor easily managed.

Is there a trace of sentimentality in the opening of the third verse? I don't think
so. A controlled and rather calculated emotion—for it is, after all, a creature
and not just a piece of inanimate mechanism that has been lost—but it is noticeable that there is a certain forcing about the embrace! And then that is followed
by the wonderful deflation which adjusts the whole perspective:

> I stroked 'is old 'ead as 'e laid in the stall,
> An' some'ow or other I felt I *must* kiss 'im!
> I've a wife an' some youngsters—'e wasn't *quite* all,
> But I *know* I shall miss 'im.

The italics are Chevalier's own, of course. Note particularly the indefinite number of youngsters—it is clear what will be missed in this entourage. Here we
have, pretty accurately summed up, the situation described in the song; and this
practical, unsentimental, rather ironic attitude to donkey and family is more than
observation, for it gets to the heart of the situation. Observation and perception
are here, far sharper than anything to be found in the yokel song just quoted or
in the jolly account of Mosedale's chestnut nag, lost though he was, too.

The first verse also presents this ironic estimate of the importance in the family
concern of donkey, wife, and children; it is the donkey who is to be carefully
doctored and fed; the singer was even prepared to give up his bed for the donkey.

There is a particularly happy relationship of words and music in the first and
third verses. The grace notes provide the basis for a sob and the words are *so*
appropriate—particularly, "nussin" and "watchin' " and "pint" and "lump"—but
in the first verse any touch of sentimentality is undercut by the words that
follow—"turned out a frost"—and in the third verse by a return to the song's
opening subject, drink as the drowner of all sorrows (which does not quite as-
sure us of the selflessness of the emotion that has caused a lump in the mourner's
throat). It is in the last line of the chorus that the true direction of the sorrow
is bluntly and economically stated: "But I think that it's rougher on me than
the moke"—and notice the musical indication, *passionata!*

This song very cleverly balances wry comic comment and a genuine sense of loss.
It manages also to analyse the nature of that loss and precisely what it is that
the mourner grieves for.

If It Wasn't for the 'Ouses in Between

Sung by Gus Elen; Words by Edgar Bateman; Music by
George Le Brunn. Copyright: Francis, Day & Hunter, Ltd.

If you saw my lit-tle back yard, "Wot a pret-ty spot!" you'd cry, It's a
pic-ture on a sun-ny sum-mer day; Wiv the tur-nip tops and cab-ba-ges wot
peo-ples does-n't buy I ___ makes it on a Sun-day look all gay. The ___
neigh-bours finks I grow 'em and you'd fan-cy you're in Kent, Or at
Ep-som if you gaze in-to the mews. It's a won-der as the land-lord does-n't
want to raise the rent, Be-cause we've got such nob-by dis-tant
views. Oh it real-ly is a wer-ry pret-ty gar-den, And

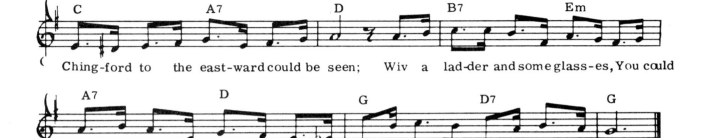

Ching-ford to the east-ward could be seen; Wiv a lad-der and some glass-es, You could see to 'Ack-ney Marsh-es, If it was-n't for the 'ous es in be-tween.

If you saw my little backyard, "Wot a pretty spot!" you'd cry,
It's a picture on a sunny summer day;
Wiv the turnip tops and cabbages wot peoples doesn't buy
I makes it on a Sunday look all gay.
The neighbours finks I grow 'em and you'd fancy you're in Kent,
Or at Epsom if you gaze into the mews.
It's a wonder as the landlord doesn't want to raise the rent,
Because we've got such nobby distant views.

CHORUS:
Oh it really is a wery pretty garden
And Chingford to the eastward could be seen;
Wiv a ladder and some glasses,
You could see to 'Ackney Marshes,
If it wasn't for the 'ouses in between.

We're as countrified as can be wiv a clothes prop for a tree,
The tub-stool makes a rustic little stile;
Ev'ry time the bloomin' clock strikes there's a cuckoo sings to me,
And I've painted up "To Leather Lane a mile."
Wiv tomatoes and wiv radishes wot 'adn't any sale,
The backyard looks a puffick mass o' bloom;
And I've made a little beehive wiv some beetles in a pail,
And a pitchfork wiv a handle of a broom.

CHORUS:
Oh it really is a wery pretty garden,
And Rye 'ouse from the cock-loft could be seen:
Where the chickweed man undresses,
To bathe 'mong the watercresses,
If it wasn't for the 'ouses in between.

There's the bunny shares 'is egg box wiv the cross-eyed cock and hen
Though they 'as got the pip and him the morf;
In a dog's 'ouse on the line-post there was pigeons nine or ten,
Till someone took a brick and knocked it orf.
The dustcart though it seldom comes, is just like 'arvest 'ome
And we mean to rig a dairy up some'ow;
Put the donkey in the washouse wiv some imitation 'orns,
For we're teaching 'im to moo just like a cah.

CHORUS:
Oh it really is a wery pretty garden,
And 'Endon to the Westward could be seen;
And by climbing to the chimbley,
You could see a cross to Wembley,
If it wasn't for the 'ouses in between.

Though the gas works isn't wilets, they improve the rural scene,
For mountains they would very nicely pass.
There's the mushrooms in the dust-hole with the cowcumbers so green,
It only wants a bit o' 'ot-'ouse glass.
I wears this milkman's nightshirt, and I sits outside all day,
Like the ploughboy cove what's mizzled o'er the Lea;
And when I goes indoors at night they dunno what I say,
'Cause my language gets as yokel as can be.

CHORUS:
Oh it really is a wery pretty garden,
And soap works from the 'ouse tops could be seen;
If I got a rope and pulley,
I'd enjoy the breeze more fully,
If it wasn't for the 'ouses in between.

In the music-hall hierarchy it is usual to find Albert Chevalier given first place among Cockney performers and to find Alec Hurley and Gus Elen trailing some way behind. In that Chevalier wrote so many of his own songs, justice is done; but I am inclined to think that in two or three songs at least, Gus Elen had material as good if not better than the very best of Chevalier's, and he had an approach which, although perhaps more restricted than Chevalier's, suited his material to perfection. Macqueen-Pope has suggested that Gus Elen's coster was closer to the Cockney way of life than was the rather more idealised version of Chevalier, but even if this is so (and a good case can be made for this argument), it is not upon the grounds of documentary exactitude alone that I would on these few occasions prefer Elen's songs to Chevalier's. It will be apparent from what I have written about "The Future Mrs. 'Awkins" of and "Jeerusalem's Dead!" that I admire these two songs very greatly, but neither is quite so perfect an expression of an attitude to life as "If It Wasn't for the 'Ouses In Between." Of Elen's other songs, " 'Arf a Pint of Ale," "It's a Great Big Shame," and "The Postman's 'Oliday" are as good as anything by Chevalier, and "Down the Road" runs as well as any music-hall song of its kind.

The words of "If It Wasn't for the 'Ouses" were written by Edgar Bateman, who also wrote those for at least two more of Elen's songs: "She's Too Good to Live Is Mrs. Carter" and "The Postman's 'Oliday." The music was written by a man who wrote a vast number of music-hall song accompaniments, including some for Marie Lloyd and Dan Leno, and also for Gus Elen's "It's a Great Big Shame":

194

George Le Brunn. Chance Newton, who knew him well, records his habit of leaving scores he was working on at the various pubs he visited en route to the particular hall he was travelling to.

"If It Wasn't for the 'Ouses" juxtaposes comedy and pathos to perfection. There is no false pity and no false pride. In addition to the juxtaposed emotional states, the song sets up a tension between daily life in the East End of London and an ideal garden state. What is so remarkable is that tension has the effect of making us laugh, and yet it never permits us to be unaware of the sordidness of the milieu—but it is not at the sordidness that we laugh. The singer does not make the mistake of abandoning himself to the ideal place he conjures up, but is able to return to reality stimulated by his imagination. The song implies the acceptance of the conditions imposed by such an environment, but with full awareness of its shortcomings and with an understanding of something better than this beyond. This is no unthinking, apathetic acceptance (as that which the governess recomends to Moll Flanders), but a lively and informed one.

The fundamental opposition within the song is very simple. The little backyard is hemmed in by row upon row of houses stretching further than the eye can see. The day itself is set in the midst of many long working days stretching before and after. In order to make it less desolate, the yard is decorated—got up—to look like a market garden, using, among many other props, the tops of the vegetables not sold from the coster's barrow during the week. That such an incongruous sight could pass for Kent, the Garden of England, is both comic and pathetic. The chorus, varied after each verse, stresses the "wery" prettiness of this garden, with—if one gets up high enough and has strong enough glasses—the added delight (again with the juxtaposition of comic and pathetic) of seeing "such nobby distant views" of delightful spots like Hackney Marshes.

The whole song is comic, but the comedy is never completely dominant. We are always made aware of the sordidness, the oppressiveness, and the sense of deprivation implicit in such a life. Despite its provenance, there is something disturbing about such a comic song and this in itself is no mean achievement. Furthermore, unlike so many music-hall songs, even the better ones, the language has a quality rarely found in this medium. Take, for example, the part-line "such nobby distant views." It is ironic, but also in a particular way, exact. In one sense it suggests a magnificent panoramic view; ironically we realise what stress is placed on "distant" and that the colloquialism, "nobby," instead of being mere local colour, accurately describes the *actual* view, "nobby" with chimney pots and similar excrescences.

Much of the humour is quiet, deflationary, and, at times, subtle. The incongruities, absurd though they are, are not gross—the dust-cart like harvest home; the pail of beetles as a beehive; the donkey with imitation horns being taught to moo like a cow; and the gas works which, if they do not have the aroma of violets, at least make pretty fair mountains—and the pathos, which the comedy offsets without obscuring, helps prevent the song becoming ridiculous. The dialect is used, as in "The Future Mrs. 'Awkins," not for the sake of its comic incongruity—so that we are invited to laugh at "error"—but because this is the normal and natural form of expression, which furthermore has subtle possibilities not possible in standard English. Thus, the first syllable of "Wembley" is delicately held, and this makes us anticipate some incongruity to match that of "chimbley." But the correct usage of "Wembley," instead of intensifying oddness, is in this sense exactly appropriate (because of the precision of the rhyme); and yet, simultaneously, it is paradoxically incongruous in implication because of the impossibility of seeing Wembley from the East End of London—even by climbing a chimney! We have a kind of complexity here which grows out of the language of the milieu and which is singularly appropriate to the song.

It is worth looking a little more closely at the language of just one verse, for it presents problems and possibilities that do not arise in standard English.

In many music-hall songs there is considerable freedom in the length of the lines used and a capacity to manipulate very long and quite short lines in the same song. This is so here. In the first verse and chorus, the number of syllables in each line varies between eight and fifteen, and rhymes are exact without ever being too pat. When part-rhyme occurs, it is not the result of inadequacy on the part of the writer, but in order to achieve (consciously or subconsciously) a particular effect—for example, deflation in "glasses/Marshes." Note how the rhyme is savoured at the end of the first verse, so drawing our attention to the *kind* of views seen from these mews.

The tone is subtly varied. The second line of verse one is slightly sentimental, but the alliterative "turnip tops" soon deflate this; and the basis of the third line sums up the conflict in the song—it is, after all, only the failure to sell all the vegetables that makes possible the creation of this mock-pastoral world. The same pattern of tones is found in the sixth line. Epsom represents the other world of fun and holiday, but this is immediately put into proper perspective when we are invited to gaze into the sordid world of the mews (where the coster's pony is kept), with its limited horizon and its implication of a workaday world. Another kind of reality breaks into the next line, for it is made clear that someone else will benefit, and the coster will have to pay, for this effort at amelioration.

In the chorus, "really is" ironically suggests just the reverse. Several of the places viewed make us wonder if there is any special delight in viewing them at all, although it ought to be pointed out that when the song was written, Wembley was a country village. However, the *relative* desirability of such a place as Hackney Marshes ironically points up the sordidness of the coster's own environment in the East End. The last line finally deflates the attempt to create an escape world in the imagination and brings a return to reality.

One of the remarkable aspects of this song is its capacity for creating an imaginary world which is never allowed wholly to possess the singer. The comedy and the deflation ensure that this imaginary world is always held at a distance, and that the implications of the real world (which are very important to the song's total effect) are never very far away. Yet, sordid though the reality is, there is about the song an affirmatory cheerfulness. The ability to laugh, not only at the sordid world (itself a quality of no mean order), but also at that desirable dream-world of the imagination, suggests a courage and perception of high distinction.

"The 'Ouses In Between" is, I am sure, one of the best songs of the music hall, and a song worthy of a very high place in the popular tradition. It has that quality, in a modest measure, of those larger and greater works of art which express a feeling for life and an attitude toward it.

'Arf a Pint of Ale

Sung by Gus Elen. Written and Composed by Charles
Tempest. Copyright: Herman Darewski Music Publishing
Co. Ltd.

Allegro moderato

I hate those chaps what talks a-bout the things what they like to drink Such as
tea and cor-fee, co-coa and milk. Why, of such things I nev-er think. I'm
plain in me hab-its and plain in me food and what I says is this: That the
man what drinks such rub-bish with his meals, Well I al-ways give him a miss. Now, for

Chorus:

Quicker

break-fast I ne-ver thinks of 'av-ing tea, I likes me 'arf a pint of
ale.   At din-ner I likes a lit-tle bit of meat, And
'arf a pint of ale.   At tea I likes a

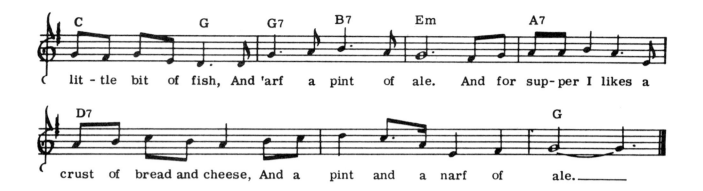

lit-tle bit of fish, And 'arf a pint of ale. And for sup-per I likes a

crust of bread and cheese, And a pint and a narf of ale.____

I hate those chaps what talks about the things what they likes to drink
Such as tea and corfee, cocoa and milk.
Why, of such things I never think.
I'm plain in me habits and plain in me food
And what I says is this:
That the man what drinks such rubbish with his meals,
Well—I always gives him a miss.

CHORUS:
Now, for breakfast I never thinks of 'aving tea,
I likes me 'arf a pint of ale.
At dinner I likes a little bit of meat,
And 'arf a pint of ale.
At tea I likes a little bit of fish,
And 'arf a pint of ale.
And for supper I likes a crust of bread and cheese,
And a pint and a narf of ale.

Now this is 'ow I looks at it and I think you'll agree with me,
I never seen a man get drunk in me life on cocoa, corfee or tea.
You think I'd pay one and eight a pound for tea—
Why the thought makes me feel queer!
When I think of what you gets for another two and six—
Such a pretty little barrel of beer.

CHORUS:
As before, but last line: And a gallon and a narf of ale.

Now folks what drinks such stuff as that are always lookin' pale;
They've pains in their tummies and they've pains in their back,
But I never have a pain with ale.
I always feels happy and I always feels right
When I've had a glass or two,
So why should I drink corfee or tea, when there's plenty of ale—
    would you?

CHORUS:
As before, but last line: And a barrel and a narf of ale.

Of all the songs in praise of drink, I like none better than this one, particularly if sung in Gus Elen's croaky Cockney voice. There is something false about the *lions comique* and their songs to Champagne, Cliquot, and Moselle; something forced about those operatic panegyrices in praise of drinking, and something over-hearty about "Beer, Beer, Glorious Beer." " 'Arf a Pint of Ale" is not so much a drinking song as a truly-felt, unsentimental song from the heart. It has a magnificent certainty about it. True, the argument is a trifle shaky (I can't quite believe that ale has never given a pain of some kind), but if the verbal logic is not strong, the emotional argument is thoroughly convincing.

It is a down-to-earth song. Drink is for supping, not for talking about. I haven't heard much conversation about the relative merits of tea and coffee, cocoa and milk, but the endless chatter about kinds of coffee is firmly put in its place here, for me at least. There is something delightful about the contemptuous dismissal of such "rubbish," and also a comic reversal of the usual attitude to drink: the weakness of this "rubbish" is that no one ever got drunk on it. I don't think we are asked to share this view, despite the preceding "And I think you'll agree with me." The agreement here is ironic, for it is not the singer's attitude that we are asked to agree with, but the fact that no one gets drunk on cocoa, coffee, or tea. Part of the strength of the song lies in its self-assurance. It presents its viewpoint so forcibly that our acceptance is simply irrelevant.

The chorus has an excellent running tune. It begins quietly and works up into a fine climax in the last line. The pattern within the chorus is repeated in the progress from one chorus to another, with the ever-larger quantities of beer that are being quaffed. It is only when we come to the barrel-and-a-half that we realise that we have been had. The exaggeration is cleverly played for. The forcefully-put point of view brooks no contradiction, so that when the last line of the third chorus comes, we find we are accepting (if not in principle agreeing with) an absurdity. And the absurdity is so triumphantly expressed that while it bursts the bubble of the fantasy that has been created, we are still left with the impression of a firmly-held, deeply-felt point of view.

The lyric is also good. The lines are long—there may be anything between thirteen and twenty syllables between rhymes—but the long line and the variable number of syllables are well managed. There is no padding, every word fulfilling a necessary function, even "What I says is this" being made relevant (compare its use with that of the "so to speak" of the second verse of "We All Go to Work But Father," or the repetition of the offer to explain in Lauder's "That's the Reason Noo I Wear a Kilt"). It is noticeable, too, how appropriately the adjectives are used. For example the use of "pretty" to describe the barrel of beer gets across the emotional, rather than the actual, description. Again "We All Go to Work But Father" provides an instructive instance of a less-happy choice of adjective in the "merry" that describes the thirty bob.

"'Arf a Pint of Ale" is particularly neat and compact, and the chorus, helped by the changes in the final lines, makes a telling climax to each verse. The total effect is particularly well-ordered. To what extent it is factually an accurate picture of the eating—and drinking—habits of those who applauded it, it is difficult to say. Doubtless there were plenty of stomachs that were not as well filled as the chorus suggests, but this is what the singer *likes*, not necessarily what he actually gets; and as an expression of an attitude, the song is convincing.

Have You Paid the Rent?

Sung by Harry Champion; Words and Music by L. Silberman, Herbert Rule and Fred Holt. Copyright: Campbell Connelly & Co. Ltd.

Allegretto

Eve - ry bod - y seems to be in trou - ble now - a - days,

Trou - ble comes to all of us in man - y, man - y ways.

Eve - ry - where you go, you'll hear a tale of woe. The

but - cher wants to meet you when the bak - er wants his dough. But there's

one thing no one ev - er wants to pay, That is why this is the lat - est

say - ing of the day: Have you paid the rent? Have you paid the rent?

Naugh - ty, naugh - ty, naugh - ty, have you paid the rent? Here's a wrink - le when the

land - lord is a - bout, Send the kid - dies down to say that

moth-er says she's out, Have you paid the rent? Have you paid the rent?
Nev-er, nev-er, tell a lie.____ If you have-n't paid the rent.
One day you'll re-pent, And you won't go to heav-en when you die.

Everybody seems to be in trouble nowadays,
Trouble comes to all of us in many, many ways.
Everywhere you go, you'll hear a tale of woe,
The butcher wants to meet you when the baker wants his dough.
But there's one thing no one ever wants to pay,
This is why this is the latest saying of the day:

CHORUS:
Have you paid the rent?
Have you paid the rent?
Naughty, naughty, naughty, have you paid the rent?
Here's a wrinkle when the landlord is about,
Send the kiddies down to say that mother says she's out.
Have you paid the rent?
Have you paid the rent?
Never, never, tell a lie.
If you haven't paid the rent,
One day you'll repent,
And you won't go to heaven when you die.

Charlie Brown was bathing in the sea and caught a cramp,
Stupid thing to do because the water was so damp.
Charlie shouted "Oh!", lobster caught his toe,
Charlie threw his arms up and he disappeared below.
Then the policeman came and at him had a look,
Said to Charlie Brown as he pulled out his little book:

Johnston spent the night out with no knocker on the door;
Got no door to hang the blessed knocker on no more.
No more roof remains, and though he still complains,
He has his dinner underneath the table when it rains.
And the neighbours' children make poor Johnston queer,
Shouting through the keyhole of the house that isn't there:

Harry Champion sang "Have You Paid the Rent?" in a rough and rather tuneless fashion. It was, as far as I can ascertain, a post-First Great War song and its lack of that sparkle that one associates with the pre-war songs and Champion's own songs about food, seems to be consistent with that assumption. I should be very surprised to find that it had been written before 1914. It could be no more than that this is a song which does not come off, but it seems to me to epitomise the kind of change that to many people seemed to come over the music halls (and the country) following the horrors of war.

The "rent" is a bogey here as it was in real life. It is not to be laughed away as is bankruptcy by the Baron Hardups of the pantomimes. Even the Johnston of the rather curious last verse doesn't seem to be making much of a go of life beneath a table—real life is not effectively distanced as it is in "The 'Ouses In Between"—and there is something ghoulish about those children who shout through a keyhole of a house that isn't there, as if it were the children that aren't there. Nevertheless, this is the most interesting verse of the song, and it does momentarily create a disturbing mood.

Champion did not stress the puns on "meat" and "dough" when singing the song, and the result is odd. They are very weak jokes, but a grimace of laughter is not extracted out of us by them as it is with Chirgwin. The reaction to Champion singing this line is one of a slight awareness of menace; it is as if one does not hear "the quotes round the pun" and the effect is oddly serious.

While the first and last verses hang together, the second verse is out of place and this is made the more apparent by the thematic relationship of the other two.

Two more points might be made, one a tiny detail, the other of wider significance. First of all, it is noticeable that the mother is instructed to send the kiddies "down" to say she is out. In England, when this song was written, most houses had living quarters on the ground floor and "out" might be expected: but this would not apply to tenement buildings.

Secondly, it will be noticed how, even in this not very successful song, the writer, like so many who wrote for the halls, is very skilful at managing lines of widely differing lengths. Additional syllables never troubled writer or singer of the halls, and the capacity to use a very long line with ease is apparent time after time.

A Little Bit of Cucumber

Sung by Harry Champion. Written and Composed by
T. W. Connor. Copyright: 1915, Francis, Day & Hunter.

I was weaned on cucumber
And on my wedding day,
Sitting down to supper when
The guests had gone away,
My old darling said to me,
"You must be hungry, Joe!
What is it you fancy?" I
Said, "Fancy! Don't you know?

CHORUS:
"I like pickled onions,
I like piccalilli.
Pickled cabbage is alright
With a bit of cold meat on Sunday night.
I can go termartoes,
But what I do prefer,
Is a little bit of cu-cum-cu-cum-cu-cum,
Little bit of cucumber."

I went flying in the air
With my old college chum.
Suddenly he said to me,
"We're bound for kingdom come!
Is there anything on your mind
Before you wear a crown?"
I began to shake and said,
"Write this confession down:

To the Lord Mayor's Banquet I
Got in one foggy day.
When I saw the grub it took
My appetite away:
"Sparrowgrass" and chaffinches,
And pigs-head stuffed with jam!
I said to the waiter there,
"You don't know who I am!

Sev'ral years of married life
Have brought me lots of joys.
I don't know how many girls,
I think it's fourteen boys.
When the last one came to town
It nearly turned my head.
It was marked with a cucumber,
And the first words that it said,

Were:

Harry Champion

Whether it really was the outstanding characteristic or not, to many people energy was the dominant trait of the music-hall—energy with exuberance—and if anyone might be said to epitomise these qualities it was Harry Champion. But too many second-rate impressions of the "good old music-hall" have begun and ended with a violently-produced version of Harry Champion's "Boiled Beef and Carrots" or "Any Old Iron," so that the vigour that certainly does exist in those songs now seems (to me, at least, perhaps suffering from a surfeit of hollow misrepresentations over the years) disproportionate and even false. Further, just as the excessive sentimentality and patriotism of many songs echo something specific of their own time, so does the excessive exuberance of many of Harry Champion's songs represent something particular to the time when they were first sung; and just as with sentimentality and patriotism of these kinds, we find such exuberance not in accord with out own conceptions of "vigour". The music-hall did have a rough vigour, and it certainly could be exuberant, but it also had many other and richer qualities and it is those that are more lasting and more interesting. In a vigorous song such as "Arf a Pint of Ale" there is something more than the crude energy which is the main ingredient of too many of Harry Champion's songs—at least as they are now interpreted by those with simple conceptions of what vigour means—a purely external energy.

I have no wish to denigrate "Any Old Iron" and "Boiled Beef and Carrots," but they have suffered from their treatment. Too often a single element, boisterousness, has been magnified out of all proportion in the presentation of these songs in order to epitomise "the music-hall." Champion's chief attribute was shared, if to a lesser degree, by many music-hall stars; but, naturally enough, as it was this idiosyncrasy that he developed, it dominated his performance. As part of a night's entertainment, Harry Champion's act was appropriate and went well; as representative of music-hall as a whole (something, of course, he never presented it as being), it is inadequate.

Champion delighted in songs about food—about pickled onions, hot meat pies, saveloys, trotters, tripe, onions, and even baked sheep's heart. But he had many other songs—"Everybody Knows Me in Me Old Brown Hat," "What a Mouth," "Beaver," "Ginger You're Barmy" (an expression alive enough to be used recently by David Lodge as the title for a novel), and that nice inversion of the Henry VIII theme, "I'm Henery the Eighth I Am," where it is the Widow Burch who has been married seven times before, and every time to a "Henery."

"A Little Bit of Cucumber" dates from the beginning of the First Great War. Its chorus fairly rattles along, and the words, in sound and meaning (especially the repetition of "pickle" and the breaking up of "cucumber"), make an appropriate mixture. The sound can be improved by singing "Cu-cum-you-come-cu-cum," as is sometimes done. In such a song the chorus bears the chief emphasis and the verses mainly serve to lead up to it. In this song, cucumber is considered a fit food for weaning, but elsewhere Harry Champion considered boiled beef and carrots more suitable for this purpose, at least as compared to tripe or steak or even a little bit of old cod's roe.

The lineation of the verses is haphazard and their order careless. The second verse might much better be placed last, and the end of the third verse is not particularly appropriate to what is to follow. Logical order is not the thought uppermost in the minds of composers of music-hall songs, not so much because of any inate inability to be logical, but simply because the medium does not make great demands upon logic, if only because the audience is not to be involved in the way that it is in the legitimate theatre. There gross illogicality jars nowadays—hence, in part, the difficulty some people have with Jacobean drama. Only very recently has legitimate drama in English endeavoured to use the illogical.

What probably struck the arranger of this song as more important than logic was that his fourth verse made possible the introduction of a loudly shouted "Where" to introduce the last chorus and so get the audience really going.

The appeal in this song, as in all those Champion had about food, was to the wholesomeness of working-class tastes (boiled beef, pickles, tripe and saveloys) as opposed to the effeteness of those who went in for social occasions (asparagus, chaffinches, and the head of the pig—stuffed with jam—instead of its feet) or the parrot food upon which vegetarians feed. These songs rejoice wholeheartedly in the pleasures of life, and to this extent are not unlike the songs of Marie Lloyd and Nellie Wallace—and, of course, Gus Elen's "'Arf a Pint of Ale," and all that went with it.

We All Go to Work But Father

Sung by J. C. Heffron. Words and Music by Leslie Reed.
Copyright: Francis, Day & Hunter, Ltd.

Oh! we are a hap-py fam-'ly and I men-tion it with pride There's fa-ther, moth-er, me and sis-ter Fan. It would be quite a mo-del group that meets round our fire-side But fa-ther he is such a la-zy man. He has not done a day's work since the morn-ing he was wed, And that is five and twen-ty years a-go. No thought of work, in fact, has ev-er got in-to his head, He's the la-zi-est man I ev-er yet did know. We

Oh! we are a happy fam'ly and I mention it with pride—
There's father, mother, me, and sister Fan.
It would be quite a model group that meets around our fireside
But father he is such a lazy man.
He has not done a day's work since the morning he was wed,
And that is five-and twenty years ago.
No thought of work, in fact, has ever got into his head,
He's the laziest man I ever yet did know.

SPOKEN: *Lazy! Why, he's bone idle! Never does anything at
all. I wouldn't care if we set him a bad example, but we
don't. In fact—*

CHORUS:
We all go to work but father
And he stays at home all day.
He sits by the fire with a quart of beer
And he smokes a ten-inch clay.
Mother works at the wash-tub,
So does my sister Fan;
I've met lazy men in my time, now and then, but a champion is our old man.

He's in three sick societies, and that's the reason why
He vows to work he never will turn out.
He groans about his liver, then he'll hug his big toe and cry,

"Good gracious! Here's my old complaint, the gout!"
It seems at work he wasn't worth above a pound a week,
Though his was always "a very trying job".
And so each club in turn he patronizes, so to speak,
By receiving just its merry thirty bob.

SPOKEN: *Yes, he belongs to the "Anti-work-yourself-to-death*
Association"; he's the secretary of it. Ah! and he abides by the rules
to the very letter, and that's one reason why:

CHORUS:
When the brokers vowed one day they'd come, because we owed some rent,
Dear mother said, "We'd better shoot the moon,"
We packed the goods upon a truck, at twelve at night we went.
But father was an obstinate old coon.
He wouldn't move an inch, he wouldn't let us take his chair,
So that we left him there you may rely.
He said our heartless conduct should be punished. I declare,
But we banged the door and shouted out, "Good-bye!"

SPOKEN: *There's cheek for you! "Our heartless conduct,"*
"miss him when he's gone," and so on! But HE didn't stop
long. When we'd got the new place cosy—all the pictures hung,
carpets down and bedsteads fixed, a knocking came at the street
door, and there were two boys, with father stuck on his chair,
and two long poles shoved underneath, like Guy Fawkes. He'd
just waited till he thought all the work was done, and then he
gave the boys two pence to bring him home. I wouldn't care
if he did something sometimes; but he doesn't.

He was standing outside our door one day with his hands
in his pockets, when a gentleman asked him the way to the
post office. Just to show how lazy he is, he pointed with his foot
and said, "Up there." The gentleman said, "If you can show
me a lazier trick than that, I'll give you half-a-crown." Our
old man replied, "Alright, come and put it in my waistcoat
pocket." I expect when he's pegging out he'll want somebody else
to draw his last breath for him. So now you can believe me when
I say:

Chorus

J.C. Heffron is best remembered for his Harry Champion-like "Where Did You Get That Hat?", a gay song of energetic absurdity. He also sang this account of family life, which, in this version, includes patter after each verse. The patter enables the chorus to be made appropriate to the verses and, after the third verse, provides a little additional comedy.

The situation in the song is not unreminiscent of that in Sean O'Casey's *Juno and the Paycock*. As in the first half of that play, the comic aspect is stressed, and though this song has none of the quality of writing or insight that marks *Juno*, and though it has nothing of the tragedy that dominates O'Casey's play, it is not completely void of ironic implications. The verses suffer from padding and from the use of words chosen for their convenience rather than their significance ("moon/coon" and "*merry* thirty bob," for example), so that the result is of no more than average quality.

It is the attitude to the lazy father that is of interest. The ideal of the united family is stated at the very beginning of the song. The family around the fireside is not just a sentimental picture, it represents an ideal state. The family has put up with this idle father for twenty-five years, but when they do reject him, he can reproach them for being heartless—and emotionally, if not logically, we cannot help but feel he might be right. Of course he turns up again, and in the final patter there is a certain pride in the way in which the two stories are told of father's idleness. The writing is loose—in the old man's reply to the gentleman for example. Indeed, only the image of someone drawing his last breath for him is at all strikingly expressed. Nevertheless, despite the weakness of the language, the relationship of the father to the family is clearly expressed, and the rejection/admiration paradox is put across at a fairly simple level.

It might seem that I am taking the words of this song as accurately representing actuality. It is true that, however inadequate, this is a work of fiction, a work of imagination, not a documentary account. Nevertheless the situation in the song accurately portrays one aspect of family life in the world from which this song sprang. It is clear that the demands made upon the family, as upon Juno and hers, cannot be shrugged off, whatever the provocation. The presentation may be comic: but father wins. The virtue that triumphs here is not that of the industrious apprentice but that of family duty, and to a certain extent it accurately expresses something of the life from which it comes in commenting upon this particular virtue rather than the middle-class virtue of industry.

The Man Was a Stranger to Me

Sung by George Formby, Sr.; Words and Music by T. W. Connor. Copyright: Herman Darewski Music Publishing Co. Ltd.

SPOKEN: *Now then Jimmy! That's the conductor's name. Get ready now.*
We'll start on this note. (Pause) Next one!

SINGS:
I never could get on with strangers somehow,
Strange faces I never could see.
Now I met a man in the street t'other day,
But the man was a stranger to me.
He said, "What's the time?", so I pulled out my watch,
I said, "Look for yourself—do, go on—
I don't think it's going." He said, "Yes it is."
In a tick after that it was gone.
As I opened my eyes, I said, "How the time flies!"
My watch in his hand I could see.
And I'd a good mind to ask him to give it me back,
But the man was a stranger to me.

SPOKEN: *I think strangers are worse than relations. (Coughs)*
I'm a little bit tight on chest tonight. Can't understand it
and I've only had one so far. I didn't hear him ask me a second
time. (Coughs) I thought as much. Get ready now, lads—second
go.

SINGS:
One night up the street I was swanking about,
When a stylish young lady dashed by.
With a heavy portmanteau she'd been for the coal,
I could tell by the piece in her eye.
She said, "Will you carry this for me, please?"
Well, I've carried parcels before
And she was good-looking, so I took on the job,
And I carried it home to her door.
The door opened wide.
She said—"Come inside;
Sit down and I'll make you some tea.
Are you fond of pastry?"—and I would have said yes,
But the girl was a stranger to me.

SPOKEN: *You was getting in a little bit late, lad, then,*
weren't you? That last note, weren't you? Well, I'll forgive
you. It doesn't matter, I got words out alright. I should
think so. I don't know, if they see a fellow dressed up
a little bit smart, they're on him. It's not safe for a
young lad to be alone. I'm getting a bit ill. Rotten me voice,
I know. I bet anybody can tell I'm a bit husky when I'm
singing. Are you finished now?

George Fromby

Of all the old recordings of music-hall stars of the period before the First Great War, none come across nowadays quite so well as those of the great Lancashire comedian, George Formby, Sr. Of course an artist like Dan Leno, who died an the very early days of commercial recording, suffers particularly from the technical imperfections of the process; and it is also understandable that many of the stage stars found it difficult to recognize and come to terms with this new medium in its early days.   Some stars made large numbers of recordings; Billy Williams's name appears on record after record—Twin, Phoenix, Cinch, John Bull, Favourite, Zonophone, Edison Bell, and Coliseum, to name but a few, many pressed in Germany.   Williams and Formby learned quickly to adapt themselves to this new medium.   Willson Disher notes that "Williams had the knack of putting his whole soul into the recording which makes you feel the singer must be inside the box," but his frequent laugh tends to jar in a way that Formby's simplicity does not.   Both, however, managed the medium well because the confidential style of their approach suited the conditions of recording.

George Formby in person must have added something to what we can now hear from his records, but even without his presence, the recordings nearly all give a complete and satisfying performance.   Furthermore his diction (except when throwing away lines in deliberately mumbled asides) is very good, and his style requires a slow and measured pace. Thus it is not difficult (as it very often is with Marie Lloyd and Dan Leno) to pick up what is being said or sung. To pick out exactly what Marie Lloyd sings in "Every Little Movement" is taxing to say the least, nor does the fault lie chiefly in the recording process; there is a slurring of certain words and an affectation of accent which suggests that her diction was not always as crystal-clear as some of those who have praised the clarity of voice of singers of the good old days suggest.

In the recordings of the two songs by George Formby, Sr. printed here, brief remarks are made by him to the conductor. In these he comments on the performance itself—a characteristic of the practice of breaking continuity in popular drama. In the recording of the first of the songs given here, Formby's famous cough can be heard. This was, for the audience, a part of the act, but Formby himself was only too well aware that it was a reminder that he was seriously ill. He was intent on keeping going long enough until his son would be able to earn a living—though not, his father hoped, on the stage.

George Formby, Sr.'s characteristic style was an engaging simplicity. It was not that he seemed to be half-witted but that he gave the impression of being almost entirely innocent of the wickedness of the world. It is this that provides the humour of the incident in which a stranger takes his watch. The joke about time flying is, of course, of ancient lineage. It occurs in Shakespeare, Gilbert and Sullivan, and Strindberg (in As You Like It, The Mikado and The Dream Play), to mention but three "legitimate" appearances; and recently Beckett has adapted the Gilbertian joke.

There is in "The Man Was a Stranger to Me" an element of pathos—although pathos is perhaps an inadequate description. It is pathetic that such shyness should prove so inhibiting. The loss of a watch in this manner is rather sad, but this is but property, whereas the innocence revealed in the reaction to the offer of pastry (with its carefully concealed innuendo) suggests that life itself is passing the singer by. There is nothing very definite on which one can put a finger (indeed that is part of the charm of the song), but the song's tone, seemingly so unaware, whether of the nature of theft or woman, makes the song, as it were, an inversion of the amoral, matter-of-fact lust for life found in the Marie Lloyd songs given here.

Part of the skill of song and singer can be seen in the lines:

> The door opened wide.
> She said—"Come inside;
> Sit down and I'll make you some tea.
> Are you fond of pastry?"

The first two very short lines are isolated by pauses, and I think it can be argued that these pauses have a different significance for the persona of the singer and for the audience. The audience can fill the pause with its speculation as to what kind of invitation this is—straightforward innuendo, carried on with the word "pastry" in the next line. But for the innocent persona of the song, this is a pause of wonderment; and it is important in performing the song that this paradox is evoked. Formby succeeds in giving a double meaning to silence—a silent pun, if you like. Furthermore the rhythm of words and pauses is particularly appropriate to the actions described. Thus, what at first sight is no more than a very simple piece of popular songwriting, has a complexity and a skilful use of resources that betokens a high level of artistic achievement.

We All Went Home in a Cab

Sung by George Formby, Sr.; Written by Harry Wincott;
Composed by George Le Brunn. Copyright: Herman
Darewski Music Publishing Co. Ltd.

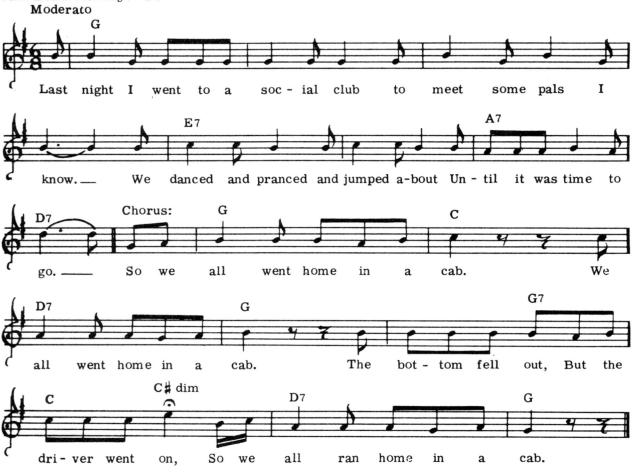

SPOKEN: *Play nice and soft for me and then you can have one when you're finished. Get ready—*

SINGS:
Last night I went to a social club
To meet some pals I know.
We danced and pranced and jumped about
Until it was time to go.
So we all went home in a cab,
We all went home in a cab.
The bottom fell out,
But the driver went on,
So we all ran home in a cab.

SPOKEN: *We did an' all. I never ran faster in me life. I'll go home no more in cabs.*

SINGS:
We went into an ice-cream shop,
Of drinks we had our sup,
With ice-cream, ginger-beer, and pop,
Until it blew us up.
Then we all went home in a tram,
We all went home in a tram.
But the guard pushed us off
And we fell on the floor,
So we didn't go home in a tram.

216

SPOKEN: *No we didn't. We went in an ambulance. I got fast in one o' tramlines and they had to get me out with a 'airpin.*

SINGS:
The other day we all set out
And we felt very fit.
We had champagne, then one chap said,
Let's make a night of it.
And we didn't get 'ome last night,
We didn't get 'ome last night.
We'd some business to do
With a man dressed in blue.
So we didn't go home last night.

SPOKEN: *He was a very nice policeman. He said he'd've let us go only in their police station they have a system and there's no friendship in business. He put a lovely pair of bracelets on my wrist and he had one on his fastened to mine. That was to stop him running away from me.*

SINGS:
Next morning we felt very dry.
We got let off that day.
The first thing that we did you'll bet,
As we got on our way,
We all went into a pub
To get some beer in there,
But it hadn't got strength
To come up the pump,
So we all came out again.

SPOKEN: *Think you've had enough now.*

The Canterbury, Lambeth, 1856

The Canterbury, entrance hall, 1856

Formby was very much the Lancashire Lad playing the provincial come to town. It was, of course, a part of his act that he should stand amazed at all that went on in the great metropolis. As a Lancashireman he *was* different and he did see things differently. Out of this sprang a gentle, ironical mocking of the pretentions of that great, colourful world of light and gaiety that loomed so large in the songs about raffish men-about-town, and existed, if to a slightly lesser extent, in reality. It was not so much that he was matter-of-fact, down-to-earth, in his approach, as that the kind of aspirations he had were so very, very modest. The best-known example is his "Playing the Game in the West," in which, after having had an exquisitely thrilling time in the West End of London, he has only one shilling left out of the two with which he began, and, because it is his night out, has no intention of returning home before a quarter to ten.

"We All Went Home in a Cab" is a good example of the kind of naive deflation of which Formby was a master. The first verse epitomises the approach. The gay life of a social club is described, in which exertion is more to the fore than grace; and this is followed by the luxury of a ride in a cab. But the bottom of the cab falls out so that the occupants have to run inside the cab to keep up with it. The result is a neat and pointed juxtaposition of irony, deflation, and farcical incongruity.

What helps to make these songs memorable is not that they are particularly witty, not that they make fanciful use of language, but that they express an irrepressible good humour in the face of the adversities they recount. A more knowledgeable or a more cunning man would not be so easily taken in, or so easily satisfied, as is the character revealed in these songs—and Formby's songs are very much to be regarded as a long sequence revealing that character rather than individual efforts as is customary in the halls. On the other hand, though so innocent, no one could possess greater equanimity, a greater capacity for taking all in his stride, than the immensely imperturbable character created by George Formby, Sr.

Although the halls struggled on for many years, their great days were already over when George Formby, Sr. died. He had not wanted his son to follow him on the stage, hoping he would earn a living in some less precarious and less heartbreaking manner. The young Formby began as a stable boy and apprentice jockey but grew too big, and, in 1920 at the age of sixteen, he gave up racing. Shortly after, his father died. Finding that other comedians were using his father's material with success (Dan Taylor and Jack Arthur both recorded some of Formby's songs), he determined to make a start on the halls working his father's act. In time he became a success in his own right and, through the media of films and television, played to far larger audiences than had his father. He died, enjoying success to the end, in 1961. But, just as his father before, he was not physically strong and had to fight constantly against ill-health.

George Formby, Jr. had a more incisive style than his father; there was about his act something wily and more knowing. Despite his undoubted success, I am inclined to think that the subtler, more seemingly innocent approach of the father revealed a greater artist. When George Formby, Sr. sings of the invitation to tea and pastry, there is no overt innuendo, whereas George Jr.'s innuendo is always pushed hard. Any trace of a leer in "The Man Was a Stranger to Me" would ruin the song and this the father completely avoids, whereas the son, in his most famous song, "When I'm Cleaning Windows," plays directly and openly upon the innuendo. Although the effect of the later song is certainly comic, something of the engaging charm of the father is lost in a performance of this kind and with that loss goes the song's subtlety. There is an edge, a sharpness, about the son's song which the cheeky gaiety does not quite offset.

Properly speaking, the song (which for reasons of copyright cannot be reprinted here) is not a music-hall song at all, though Formby did sing it in the halls. An l.p. recording of Formby singing this song was issued a year or two ago. It began life in 1937 in the film "Keep Your Seats Please" which Formby made for Associated Talking Pictures at Ealing Studios (one of a sequence of films that starred either Formby or Tommy Trinder and which paved the way for the great post-war series of Ealing comedies).

The song does not have a chorus, as this is usually understood (indeed, the verses are marked "Chorus" in Lawrence Wright's edition). Instead there is a refrain that is repeated in the middle of each verse. In addition "When I'm Cleaning Windows" occurs regularly but not mechanically. There are also two supernumary introductory lines to the song as a whole. This arrangement is a clever adaptation of the usual music-hall pattern to the requirements of the film medium. Formby accompanied himself with great skill on a ukelele, and he played this between the first and second verses and, more briefly, at the end of the third verse before the final "When I'm cleaning windows."

There is a greater and more obvious use of innuendo in this song than in those printed here which were sung by Marie Lloyd, and, as has already been implied a trace of a leer lies behind some of the lines. This is particularly apparent in the second verse, which is but a rag-bag of assorted ideas.

The song is comic but it does not, as do some of the great music-hall songs, have either complex theatrical qualities or conflicts of tone, nor does it illuminate the way of life with which it deals. It is a calculated piece of work, well-turned in its way—note, for example, the frequent and skilful use of rhyme to enable the innuendo to be put across with full effect—and it gets the most out of the situations it describes. As a song for the kind of persona George Formby, Jr. adopted, it is well-done but it is only as good as its comic twists. Its life will depend upon the degree to which its kind of innuendo continues to intrigue. It lacks that element of the life from which it springs that is to be found in the best music-hall (and folk) songs, an element which not only enriches but plays some part in making it possible for the song to live on.

Half-Past Nine
or
My Wedding Day

Sung by Nellie Wallace; Written and Composed by Charles
Collins. Copyright: Herman Darewski Music Publishing
Co. Ltd.

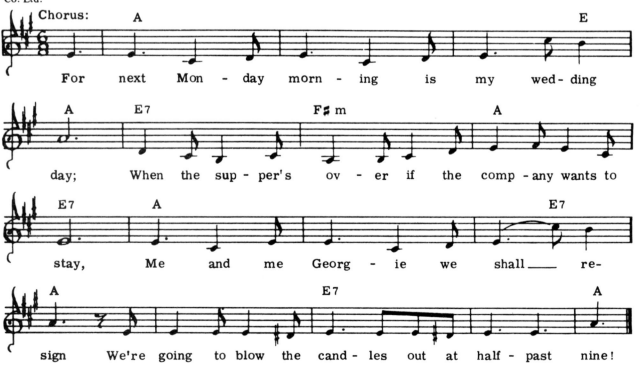

Chorus: For next Monday morning is my wedding day; When the supper's over if the company wants to stay, Me and me Georgie we shall ___ re-sign We're going to blow the candles out at half-past nine!

I'm longing for next Monday 'cos I'm going to tie the knot
With little Georgie Puddingy-Pie, a nice young man I've got.
And when the parson says the word that makes two into one,
I want you all to just come round and join us in the fun.

CHORUS:
For next Monday morning is my wedding day;
When the supper's over if the company wants to stay,
Me and me Georgie we shall resign,
We're going to blow the candles out at half-past nine!

SPOKEN: *Oh d-d-d-d-d-d-dear! I feel so excited today. No
wonder girls, one doesn't get married very often, y'know.
At least, I don't (Very rapidly, chuckling) Oh d-d-d-d-d-dear,
What a life, what a life!*

Now when we get back from the church, and the friends have all been in,
And wished us joy and happiness in little drops of gin—(Hiccup) Oh dear!
We want to both be on our own, I think it's only fair.
You may be sure that we don't want a lot of people there

Chorus

SPOKEN: *Oh d-d-d-d-dear! Oh d-d-d-d-dear! I say, how do
you like my dress, girls? Very becoming isn't it? I love the
two-piece. It's so becoming to the slim figure.
I love the slim figure. I love the long lining at the side here.
It's one of Selfridge's, you know, one of Selfridge's.
Specially from dear old Gordon. He's a darling boy, isn't he?
This is my feather boa. D-d-d-d-d-dear! This weather plays
havoc with your clothes. All out of curl. Pure down, too,
pure down, all these feathers are. That's why it's so flat.*

Now after we've had supper, I shall soon shut up the show.
I will cut them all a slice of cake, and tell them all to go.
And when I take the Vee of orange blossoms off my head—(*Chuckles*)
I shall tell them all its time that we—were fast asleep in bed.

Chorus

Left: Marie Campbell, Top: Madge Girdlestone, Right: Ruby Verdi, Bottom: Nellie Wallace.

One of the legendary figures of the music hall is the Vital Spark, Jenny Hill, who died in 1897. She won a remarkable reputation as a serio[1] and was famous, in Chance Newton's words, as the "most artistically 'realistic' comic and pathetic singer on the music-hall boards." Chance Newton knew Jenny Hill well; he also knew Nellie Wallace, and, in writing of her, he compared her to Jenny Hill. Her "slavey impersonations," he said, "are equal to the comic specimens which were given in the past by that great all-round artist, Jenny Hill"; and he concludes: "I can give no higher praise to Miss Wallace than this."

[1]'Serio' (from 'serio-comic') was the name given to a performer whose act was simultaneously comic and serious (or pathetic).

Nellie Wallace's most remarkable ability was a capacity for investing the gauche and awkward with a warmth and humour that avoided ridiculing the less fortunate in place and form. Her voice, like Gus Elen's or George Formby Sr.'s, comes across remarkably well in recordings, although she had the advantage of being able to make recordings when techniques were good. Inevitably a recording lacks her curious figure, with its odd clothes and tatty boa, but at least in her recording of "Half-Past Nine," we hear about them.

In her recording the verses are sung in short, sharp, staccato bursts into which are slipped giggles, chuckles, and hiccups. When it comes to the chorus, however, Miss Wallace adopts a different technique. Instead of short bursts of song, independent phrases, she launches into a confident, joyous sweep of triumph as she regales us with the events planned for the ensuing Monday. Perhaps the song ought to be seen as a later victory after the disappointment of being left, like Vesta Victoria, "Waiting at the Church." As in that song, the point at issue is the consummation of marriage, and it is presented with rich enjoyment. Note, for example, the "little drops of gin" to which she refers with such coy relish in her performance.

The chorus follows the verses well because it completes the events arranged for the Monday; these are described at three different stages in the three verses. In singing the final chorus, Miss Wallace completes the air of triumph by breaking into a kind of yodel in place of words. The band plays the next two lines to a couple of snatches of patter from the singer—"Let the festivities begin . . . partners for the next two-step"—and then she sings the last line. The effect is one of tremendous exuberance, eclipsing the deliberately hesitant opening appropriate to the rather pathetic bride-to-be with which the song beings.

The patter is spoken very fast in a sharp, tightly-controlled voice. Selfridge's is (as it was then) one of London's largest department stores and Gordon Selfridge was its founder.

Although so very different in tone, "Half-Past Nine" shares with the songs of Marie Lloyd printed here the same delight in fleshly pleasure, though without quite the same kind of suggestiveness of the earlier songs.

Nellie Wallace's was not the first "Half-Past Nine." I am indebted to Mr. Peter Gammond for the words of an earlier song with the same title. It was published in 1893 by Francis, Day & Hunter, and was written by Wal Pink and George Le Brunn.

> Sweet are vacation, they bring variations,
> So thought John Tompkins, a clerk,
> As off like a rocket went he cash in pocket,
> Released from his dull office work.
> He went not to seaside, nor to Deeside,
> But to a village less famed,
> Where he, although married, a love affair carried
> On with a girl who exclaimed:
>
> I'll be there, love, at half-past nine.
> I'll be there be it wet or fine.
> I'm your true love and you are mine
> So meet me down the lane tonight at half-past nine.

Ah, those innocent naughty nineties!

Heaven Will Protect an Honest Girl

Sung by Gracie Fields; Written by R. P. Weston and Bert
Lee; Composed by Harris Weston. Copyright: 1933,
Francis, Day & Hunter, Ltd.

On the day I left the vil-lage, my dear mo ther whis-pered,"Nell, Take this

piece of bread and drip-ping and your fare _____ And re-

mem - ber when in Lon-don, though you're just a ser - vant gel, you're a

blond, the sort that gen - tle -men en - snare. _____ With your

youth and fa - tal beau -ty, When you get to Wa - ter -loo, There'll be

crowds of dukes and mil-lion-aires all wait - ing there for you. But

On the day I left the village, my dear Mother whispered, "Nell,
    Take this piece of bread and dripping and your fare,
And remember when in London, though you're just a servant gel,
    You're a blonde, the sort that gentlemen ensnare.
With your youth and fatal beauty, when you get to Waterloo,
There'll be crowds of dukes and millionaires all waiting there for you—But:

FIRST CHORUS:
"Heaven will protect an honest gel,
An an-gi-el will guard you, little Nell.
    When these rich men tempt you, Nelly,
    With their spark-el-ling Moselly,
Say 'Nay-nay!' and do be very care-fu-el!
And if some old bloated blase roue swell
Says 'I'll kiss you, we're alone in this hotel,'
    Breathe a prayer he shall not do it
    And then biff him with the cruet,
Then Heaven will protect an honest gel!"

When I got to wicked London in my little clogs and shawl,
  And my bit of bread and dripping in my hand,
I went up to that big Lifeguard on his horse outside Whitehall,
  And I asked him to direct me to the Strand.
But he didn't even answer he just sat there with his sword,
In a helment that had whiskers on, so I said "Thank the Lord—For:

SECOND CHORUS:
"Heaven will protect an honest gel,"
And I reached Piccadilly safe and well.
    There I saw a red light showing,
    But across I started going,
When a P'liceman pulled me back I nearly fell.
"You're a silly little fool," he starts to yell,
"Don't you know what that red light means?" I said, "Well,
    Red's for danger, if you please sir,
    But don't switch it on for me, sir,
'Cause Heaven will protect an honest gel!"

*Optional second verse chorus (or first chorus of third verse if
three verses are used):*

Heaven will protect an honest gel,
That night I got a job at some hotel,
    But the chef was most improper
    For he sat me on the copper
And said, "Kiss me or I'll boil you, little Nell."
But I slapped him on the face—and in I fell,
And I came up for the third time with a yell,
    "In the soup I'm going to simmer,
    But I'll come out clean and slimmer,
For Heaven will protect an honest gel!"

I wandered round Li-cester Square from six o'clock till nine,
    But no millionaire came tempting me to stray,
"If he does", I thought, "I'll let him take me to the Ritz to dine,
    Then I'll gollop up his tripe and run away."
Eeh by gum! I did feel hungry! Eeh! I hadn't had a bite
Since my bit of bread and dripping, and I knew that Ma was right—For:

THIRD CHORUS:
Heaven will protect an honest gel.
Next day I pawned my shawl in Camberwell,
    Then my skirt and blouse, I sold 'em
    And went tramping back to Oldham;
When a fortnight passed, then I rang at the bell.
"Eeh, but Mother dear," I said, "it's little Nell,
I have lost my sole—my uppers too, as well—
    And I've walked home in my undies.
    But I'll tell my Class on Sundays
That Heaven will protect an honest gel!"

The great days of the English music hall were those prior to the First Great War. Various reasons have been given for its death—competition from musicals, from films (especially talkies), from radio; the blow struck to that sense of sheer gaiety which some people believe existed before the First Great War (or the General Strike of 1926), Robert Tressell notwithstanding, and never since recovered; or that no longer were there any artists of star quality developed. No single answer is adequate, and some of these (the last, for example) seem to me downright wrong. Clarkson Rose suggests correctly (in *Red Plush and Greasepaint*) that the causes of its end were many; and, significantly, some were to be found within music hall itself. It lost its drive, it no longer developed, it became stereotyped, some artistes became lazy, it tried to be too grand and, worst of all, respectable (particularly under the aegis of Sir Oswald Stoll). In trying to become "legitimate" as it were, it may, I believe, have lost its intimate link with the world from which it had originally sprung; furthermore, continued in the old way, it could no longer—or rather, it *did* no longer—reflect what motivated that world. Doubtless the social changes wrought by the Great War and the arrival of talking films and radio were severe blows to music hall, but I am sure Clarkson Rose is right when he points to the weakening from within. After all, the gramophone was far from superseded by radio, despite the gloomy prognostications of experts in the late twenties.

Music hall has virtually died, although it retains an antiquarian interest and still attracts those anxious to savour what they take to be the spirit of the Good Old Days. But if the halls have gone, popular drama in other forms has grown very strong in recent years in England. It is not difficult to trace a line of descent from the patter and the duo acts of music hall through such radio half-hours as *Bandwaggon* of pre-1939 days, *Itma* and *Much Binding* of the war years, Hancock, the Goons, and *Round the Horne* of more recent years on radio, to television programmes based on those of radio, to the many original half-hour comedy creations of television itself. Recently, too, there has been a growth of pub and club entertainment: in a sense we are back where we came in a little over a hundred years ago.

One thing is certain: the star material was available after the First Great War. As the music halls did not die a sudden but a slow and painful death, there was just enough enticement, despite the Depression (or perhaps because of it), to persuade men and women to continue with a career on the halls or to set out as popular entertainers. Radio stars such as Tommy Handley and Arthur Askey (the latter still going strong) were originally either of the halls or began in concert parties or minstrel shows during or just after the war. Perhaps the greatest of all the stars between the wars was Gracie Fields, who without question had the capacity and the star quality possessed so abundantly by Marie Lloyd. But, for many, the dying of the halls was painful, even to the point of suicide. One of the best and most resourceful comedians between the wars (who outlasted the tearing down of the hall with which he was particularly associated, the Metropolitan in the Edgware Road, London—) can easily be traced through recording after recording made over a period of thirty or more years, often before audiences. It is almost depressing to hear the closing stages of this sequence, when he is performing outside the halls. He remains the irrepressible cheeky chappie, but he has to work harder with his audience and there is a sense of weariness that is not entirely attributable to his age. The conditions had changed more than the performers.

Of the last performers, the greatest was Gracie Fields. She had the power of holding an audience in the hollow of her hand. Year after year, in favourable and adverse circumstances, she could set an audience laughing or crying in the best

Robsonian manner. She was able to sing pathetic songs, comic songs, "The Lord's Prayer" and "Ave Maria," and top it all off with grotesque comedy without her act seeming at any moment to be incongruous. As with many later performers it is still possible to hear her acts given before ordinary, paying audiences; to hear the response she could evoke in, say, the recording made by HMV in 1933 at the Holborn Empire (and given the dignity of being issued in a khaki album with gold lettering—just like a piano concerto!), is still a remarkable experience.

It is appropriate, then, to end this selection of music-hall songs with one made famous at the beginning of the 1930s by the last great star of the halls, happily still with us. Recently she sang in a television programme broadcast from the home of television variety, the London Palladium, to commemorate the tenth year of commercial television in England. The song also is appropriate. It is a good example of the capacity of popular drama to laugh at itself, in this case at its cherished sincerity—and it recalls (especially in the split syllables of verse one) the tone and technique of the "Villikins" of a century before. Indeed this song is best when closest in style to "Villikins."

Perhaps, too, we can consider the Honest Girl as epitomising the old halls. At the moment the spirit of the halls is back, not after a fortnight but after a run of a hundred years, ringing the bell for mother. And like Little Nell with the cruet, for music hall too, self-help is the first step to divine protection.

Gracie Fields

Afterword

In the commentaries I have usually concerned myself with a single song at a time, although occasionally comparisons have been made and some matters of wider concern considered. I wish now to bring together some of the points scattered throughout the commentaries to see whether it is possible to reach a few tentative conclusions about music-hall songs and about the dramatic and critical issues raised.

All the songs presented in this volume seem to me interesting and singable, and a number are among the best of their kind. Nevertheless the selection has been made to bring out the quality and nature of most kinds of music-hall song rather than on the basis of selecting a "top fifty". If the poorest songs are omitted, there are many others as good as the best of those given here. It will be obvious that some songs are more mundane than others, and time after time the writing lacks precision. Choruses are sometimes carelessly related to verses and songs are frequently banal and incoherent.

Unfortunately for music-hall songs, they do not respond to the kind of treatment meted out by literary critics of whatever persuasion they be. The languages of criticism may, with some facility, point out weaknesses, but rarely what, in this particular genre, has life and value. Possibly this is an extreme case of the difficulty so much criticism has in dealing with the dramatic and especially the comic (unless it be ironic); partly it is caused by an unwillingness to take into consideration anything but what appears on the page, partly it is the result of the insufficiency of our critical approaches. The upshot is that the music-hall song is grossly underrated by the aesthetic critic. Clearly no individual song, however sympathetic one is to the genre, can do more than give a brief insight, make a slight comment, on some aspect of human experience. These are songs, not epics. It is not a case, *pace* Peacock (or rather, his Mr. Derrydown), of "Chevy Chase" giving "deeper insight into the truth of things" than *Paradise Lost.*

Clearly, most music-hall songs, like most writing of every period, are of no merit. Even the best music-hall songs are prone to the faults of their kind: imprecise use of language, crudeness of style and structure. These must be faults that loom large before the critic. But the significance of a music-hall song does not lie solely in the implication it has for the theatre and for the writers of legitimate drama (though these aspects are important). The best music-hall songs, within the limits of their compass, express a reaction to some kind of human experience, real or imaginative, in a way peculiar to themselves. Understanding and isolating that experience and its expression is inadequately and often inaccurately done by conventional (if divergent) literary critical approaches; and I hope I have, in the commentaries, suggested some ways in which the experience these songs reveal may be perceived.

It will be obvious that I have contravened certain popular critical fallacies. In discriminating between "It's Alright in the Summertime" and "Waiting at the Church," I have brought into the discussion our experience of the outside world, and have suggested that we can bring to "Cushie Butterfield" and "The Future Mrs. 'Awkins" our awareness of the literary tradition of courtship poems. The significance of Vesta Tilley impersonating a male has been allowed to influence the "words on the page" of "Following in Father's Footsteps"; and the significance of the context in which the sentimental song was sung on the halls has been referred to. The different reactions of singer and audience to a pause—making a "silent pun"—in Formby's "The Man Was a Stranger to Me," involve effect upon an audience (and perhaps even the intention of the singer?).

Evaluation of the music-hall song must also take into account its deliberate use of the conflict of tones and Robsonian juxtaposition. Clearly, confusion may result, as in "Nanny," but this kind of conflict can be dramatic and significant, as it is in "The 'Ouses In Between" and "Jeerusalem's Dead!" Conflict of tone is, of course, to be found in literature more formal than music-hall song, especially in drama. What may deceive the conventional critic is the degree to which, in the music hall, subtle and percipient effects may be achieved by the use of elements which, taken in isolation, will seem crude and exaggerated.

What else can the music-hall song offer?—and the importance is on "can," for it must be stressed that, as in every form of writing, one is fortunate if a tiny proportion of the mass proves significant.

Although much music-hall writing lacks order and coherence, the writers and singers of music-hall songs were as adept as were their distant forbears in managing a very long line of verse and in manipulating lines of variable length. Despite their frequent imprecise use of language, the music hall, in its songs and acts, paradoxically reveals a fascination with language. In this volume this is apparent in the songs and patter of Dan Leno, T. E. Dunville, George Chirgwin, Little Tich, George Robey, and Emil Clare, and it is to be found in isolated examples in unlikely contexts—in George Formby, Sr. and Harry Lauder, for example. Furthermore this is a characteristic that contemporary popular drama has not lost. It is remarkable how much the popular drama of the past hundred years has depended for its enjoyment on playing with language; language has become a game in its own right again, as it was in the Shakespearean age. Often this is not the kind of playfulness that appeals to the conventional critic, but it cannot be denied that for performer and audience it provides intense delight in language—in rhyme, nonce-words, puns good and bad, association, extension of meaning, alliteration, spoonerisms, malapropisms, and even syntax and accidence.

This interest in language has two implications. First of all it maintains, to a very much greater degree than has the *theatre de boulevard*. an awareness of language as language. In music halls and in popular drama generally, language has developed a vigour of its own kind. It is not only a means of communication but a form of being in its own right.

Secondly, play with words and the use of innuendo demand of an audience a capacity for intent listening. Recently the English dramatic critic, J.C. Trewin, complained (justifiably) that audiences had become lazy: "Audiences have lost the Elizabethan-Jacobean art of acute listening." Plays such as *Timon of Athens* and *Too True to be Good,* wrote Mr. Trewin, demand our full attention, but don't always get it. This is certainly true of audiences of legitimate drama, but I do not believe it would be as correct of popular dramatic audiences. The popular drama, in retaining its delight in language, demands of an audience close listening. It is just possible, rather ironically, that the audience of which Mr. Trewin rightly complained had come expecting to "hear" stars of popular drama and were unprepared for Shaw. Adequate evidence is not available and so it is not possible to be sure whether the fault lay in Shaw's third act, in a performance in the process of being tightened up, or in an audience feeling its expectancy tricked. Or, of course, perhaps the audience *did* listen, but did not like what it heard.

A common and often fair criticism of the material of popular drama is that it is closely dependent upon high, more consciously artistic, literature. Burlesque and parody are obvious examples, and attention has been drawn to a technique used by Dickens for Mr. Jingle of *The Pickwick Papers* (which is also to be found in one of T.E. Dunville's songs) and it has been suggested that Robey's "Prehistoric Man" is like watered-down Gilbert and Sullivan. While much popular drama is a degenerate form of something else, it could be argued that some—if not most—of the literature of any age is imitation in various degrees of pallidity of what at the time is thought to lead. Thus, although there is imitation and parody in the music hall, I hope I have shown that some music-hall songs have something original and idiosyncratic to offer.

Music-hall songs reveal a number of characteristics which, though not obviously apparent in every song, are found frequently. There is, first of all, an acceptance of things as they are. This is not, however, apathetic acceptance (though political concerns are rare in the halls and when found, are baldly over-simplified) but a down-to-earth awareness of the real conditions of the life lived. This awareness can range from the sexuality (rather than the sensuality) extolled by Marie Lloyd, to cheerful amorality, to an awareness of the significant "economic issues" of "Jeerusalem's Dead!" With this goes a thoroughgoing wholeheartedness in many songs—in Marie Lloyd's for fleshly delights, in Champion's for food, in Elen's for ale. This awareness of life as it is, leads to that remarkable capacity of popular drama for self-deflation. This may take the form of songs or acts within the tradition (in the manner of Herbert Campbell or such songs as "I Live in Trafalgar Square"), or it may be self-directed, as in "Wotcher 'Ria."

The dramatic implications of music hall are varied. Their development from tavern bars and supper rooms meant that the performer made his appeal directly to the audience, and this tradition continued even when the music halls imitated the architecture of the legitimate theatres of nineteenth-century London. What is even more remarkable is that even in programmes involving "fourth-wall" sketches on television, popular dramatic comedians have continued to break the continuity and make a separate, direct appeal "through the camera" to the audience at home. It is easy to see this technique going back to Elizabethan times, where the association of legitimate and popular drama— "the writ and the liberty"—was closer than it is now. This may, in a song or monologue, be taken a stage further (as in Leno's, Little Tich's, and Robey's songs and patter given in this volume). In directly addressing the audience, the performer may break the continuity of that direct address by dissociating the persona adopted from that of the comedian's own self; this demands of an audience the capacity to respond in two different ways simultaneously. He may even, as in the Max Miller extract given at the end of the commentary on Leno's "The Swimming Master", break the dramatic illusion completely by drawing attention to his having lost his place. And even get a laugh from that!

232

S.L. Bethell in his book, *Shakespeare and the Popular Dramatic Tradition,* drew attention to the capacity of popular dramatic audiences[1] for multiconscious apprehension. This can be seen from the songs discussed in this volume in the way in which the performer can present himself as himself and in character simultaneously; from the ability to apprehend the fanciful and the realistic simultaneously; and from the way in which it is possible to present, at the same time, conflicting tones—comic and pathetic, serious and debunking.

George Robey, in his autobiography, *Looking Back on Life,* recalls the "ludicrous irrelevance" of the backcloths in front of which music-hall singers performed. "Picture me," he says, "singing such lines as:

> You can tell her by the pimple,
> The pimple on her nose!

in front of a cloth that depicted Melrose Abbey by moonlight!" After giving several more examples, he comments:

> These backcloths were part of the queerness of the
> halls in those early 'nineties, and I can't think why we
> tolerated them so long. In the (legitimate) theatres such
> anomalies wouldn't have been tolerated for ten min-
> utes. Can you imagine Henry Irving asking "Is that a
> dagger that I see before me?" in front of a cloth representing
> the Epsom racecourse on Derby Day?

That such anomalies were tolerated may be no more than a product of insensitivity or artistic unconcern on the part of performer, producer and audience. Nevertheless, once expediency, thoughtlessness, and insensitivity had permitted such ludicrous irrelevance, it is clear that, for the most part, audience and performer were able to dissociate what was irrelevant from what was relevant to the act. Whether the popular audience's capacity for involvement and detachment that I have described earlier made such dissociation possible, or whether it fostered that capacity, it is difficult to tell. Such "confusions of tone," rath-

[1] I use "the popular dramatic audience" as a shortened form of "the audience attending a popular dramatic presentation" as opposed to an audience attending a legitimate drama. Although there may be social distinctions between such audiences (especially at certain times and places), I do not suggest that individual members of each kind of audience have different capacities for comprehending popular and legitimate drama. It is not the individuals who differ, but the conventions of performance. Thus the same individual (or audience) that can laugh at a music-hall comedian who forgets his act and makes a joke about it, will be as put out as the legitimate actor who forgets his part in the *theatre de boulevard.*

er like those of Harry Lauder's "Nanny," are part and parcel of popular drama. Often the confusion is gross or merely fortuitous (as in the case of the back-cloths), but it seems possible to make, out of confusion, contrast and con-flict—and to be able to develop the capacity to offset involvement and detach-ment; this the music hall did do.

This kind of detachment is a purely theatrical quality in the music hall. It does not have any of the social and political implications associated with the Brechtian *Verfremdungseffekt*. In discussing "alienation effect" in *A Short Organum for the Theatre,* Brecht might, in section 42[1], not only be describing the kind of acting tried out at the Schiffbauerdamm Theatre in Berlin between the wars, but that capacity for wonderment and surprise at the ordinary that I have suggested Dan Leno was able to create:

> A representation that alienates is one which allows
> us to recognize its subject, but at the same time makes
> it seem unfamiliar.

But just as the social aims of the old devices for effecting alienation that Brecht describes are different from Brecht's aims, so are his different from those of the music hall. In the English popular drama the technique is designed solely to entertain; for Brecht:

> This technique allows the theare to make use in its rep-
> resentations of the new social scientific method known
> as dialectical materialism.

Some time later, Brecht, in his *Appendices to the Short Organum,* modified this last section, and in its reworking (not discovered until after his death) it is possible to see, in the first sentence, Brecht's concern with dialectics and, in what follows, a summary of many of the characteristics associated with music hall in particular and popular drama in general:

> The theatre of the scientific age is in a position to make
> dialectics into a source of enjoyment. The unexpected-
> ness of logically progressive or zigzag development, the
> instability of every circumstance, the joke of contradic-
> tion and so forth: all these are ways of enjoying the
> liveliness of men, things and processes, and they heighten
> both our capacity for life and our pleasure in it.

[1]Quotations are from *Brecht on Theatre,* translated by John Willett.

> Every art contributes to the greatest art of all, the art
> of living.

Alienation, as Brecht explained, produces an effect the exact opposite of empathy, which is the basis of *rapport* between audience and the stage in the conventional theatre; and, on a number of occasions, Brecht deprecated empathy (though sometimes with qualifications).

It will be clear that the aim and the effect of breaking continuity in English music hall is quite different from the effect of Brechtian alienation. In the music hall the aim is simple—to raise a laugh—but the effect is more complex. Involvement is broken in the act (a condition anathema to the *theatre de boulevard*), and a different kind of relationship is developed between the person of the performer and the audience rather than with his persona. But the detachment from the persona (the breaking of empathy) is not at the expense of final, overall involvement; for the audience, though momentarily detached and alienated, becomes thereafter more deeply involved.

Thus, despite John Osborne's attempt at *Verfremdungseffekt,* the audience of *The Entertainer* becomes not alienated but doubly involved, because his use of the technique is too closely associated with the technique of his subject matter, the music hall.

Although insensitivity doubtless played a large part in permitting the use of backcloths like those described by George Robey, insensitivity is not the whole answer. Popular dramatic audiences are able to direct their involvement to what is relevant. Robey is quite right in saying that Irving would not have played Macbeth before a backcloth of Epsom racecourse, and that an audience would have hooted at such a conjunction. This does not mean that an audience of *Macbeth* is thereby more sensitive than a music-hall audience; indeed in some ways it is less flexible in its reactions than is an audience for popular drama. Such a backcloth would be impossible in the legitimate theatre in these circumstances because the tradition of congruity is so strong, especially since the growth of realistic drama and the advent of films. While not being particularly anxious to have a Macbeth perform before a painting of Epsom racecourse, it is a pity that the objection should be made on the grounds of realism. It is not the realistic presentation of these scenes (or of many in contemporary drama) that ought to be important in a production, but the creative and imaginative aspects; it is the sense of wonder that should matter, not the likeness to life. In this, the popular still has something to offer the legitimate.

The qualities and the implications of music hall and other popular dramatic forms can only be revealed by thoughtful criticism. Only the most narrow-minded critic would endeavor to understand and evaluate every literary form in exactly the same way, dismissing all that did not fit his prescription. It is essential that a mode of discourse be used which is appropriate to the work being considered. Thus, if verbal complexity is taken as a critical tool—or indeed elevated to being *the* critical tool—it will be found more illuminating for a few works than for many others.

There are difficulties which the critic has to overcome in examining music-hall songs and acts. First of all, the use of language—*the* medium of literary art—is usually loose, and this might also be said of the music. Secondly, there is a delight in badness; and thirdly, there is the incapacity of music hall to face certain kinds of reality.

There is no avoiding the difficulty posed for the critic by loose writing. A few songs do show verbal precision and careful musicianship, but too often expediency and carelessness are in evidence—after all, any composer faced with the necessity of writing the instruction "Till ready" can hardly be admonished for lapsing into banality. With these songs that do have something to offer but express it carelessly, we can but grasp at what is good and wish that the expression had been more polished. On the other hand it has to be remembered that such polish is the product of a kind of experience with which these songs are not concerned. Possession of the one might well drive out the other—that intimate experience with the life at the back of these songs—and it is that link that is so valuable.

The delight in literary badness is remarkably vigorous in popular drama, and it has to be accepted on its own terms and not those of the all-knowing critic. What matters is the delight, not the badness. I have suggested in the commentaries that this delight in badness may stem from a sense of rebelliousness towards authority; and this and the extent to which it reveals an awareness of language, by implication and as a means of expressing such an attitude, may best defend and explain it.

Music hall ignored, or failed to deal adequately with, some aspects of life. (So did Jane Austen.) In its patriotic songs, in songs from the heart, and even in its attitude to some fallen public figure (such as Sir Charles Dilke), it could be grossly one-sided; although this was a characteristic of the halls, it is not the whole story.

To an extent not found in the legitimate theatre, music hall was capable of self-regulating its excesses. If it did not deal with certain aspects of life, it was, I suspect, because it did not find them particularly relevant to its experience of life. Sophisticated political revue must have a greater meaning and appeal for those who are involved, or who feel involved, in the political struggle than it can have for those who feel resigned to be affected by political decisions but unable to influence them. By and large this was the position of the working class when the music halls were at their height. Similarly, sophisticated sexual witticisms will appeal more to those whose sexual standards are not rigidly defined. The music-hall song was the product of a way of life which could do little to affect political thought and whose moral code, though not coincident with that of other classes in England, was firmly rooted, if not always firmly followed. The edges of rightness and wrong were more sharply defined than amongst the more sophisticated.

What, then, may be found in the better music-hall songs? They make skilful use of tonal complexity in a way that takes one back to the great and lesser drama of Elizabethan and Jacobean days, but which has only recently been discovered again by our legitimate drama. Compare, for example, the tonal complexities described in the commentaries with those to be found in, say, Marlowe's *The Jew of Malta*, or in Act III Scene I of *The Merchant of Venice*, or in such a lesser play as Ford's *The Fancies Chaste and Noble*. They are able to present simultaneously the worlds of fancy and reality; they can offset involvement and detachment; often they are self-critical and have an excellent capaciry for ironic self-deflation; they are often richly aware of the peculiarities and possibilities of the English tongue; but, above all, at their best, they express in a way that no outside observer can, however sympathetic to it he may be, the experience of that way of life from which they spring. At its best, in revealing this experience, the music-hall song has wholeheartedness and warmth, independence and tolerance, ironic deflation, and a fine balance between the comic and pathetic aspects of any experience.

Like every art, music hall can, in Brecht's words, make its contribution to the greatest art of all: the art of living.

Bibliography

This list gives details of all the books that have been helpful to me in preparing my commentaries and includes all those to which direct reference is made in the text. George Rowell's *The Victorian Theatre* contains a particularly useful bibliography of books published before its own date of issue (1952).

George W. Alltree, *Footlight Memories,* n.d.
Jean Anderson, ed., *Late Joys at the Players' Theatre,* 1963.
Max Beerbohm, *Around Theatres,* 1922.
S. L. Bethell, *Shakespeare and the Popular Dramatic Tradition,* 1944.
Rudi Blesh and Harriet Janis, *They All Played Ragtime,* 1958.
J. B. Booth, *Old Pink 'Un Days,* 1924.
    "Master" and Men—Pink 'Un Yesterdays, 1927
    London Town, 1929.
    The Days We Knew, 1943.
Dion Clayton Calthrop, *Music Hall Nights,* 1925.
Albert Chevalier, *Albert Chevalier,* 1896.
    Before I forget, 1901.
Arthur Croxton, *Crowded Nights—and Days,* n.d.
Jacques Damase, *Les Folies du Music-Hall,* 1962.
Peter Davison, "Contemporary Drama and Popular Dramatic Forms" (1963) in
    Aspects of Drama, 1965.
    "Dead and Never Called Me Mother," *Mermaid,* 1967.
    "A Briton True? A short account of patriotic songs
    and verse as popular entertainment." *Alta,* University
    of Birmingham Review, Spring 1970.
M. Willson Disher, *Clowns and Pantomimes,* 1925.
    Winkles and Champagne, 1938.
    Victorian Song, 1955.
Charles Dibdin Jnr., *The Farmer's Wife,* 1814 (*The London Stage,* IV, c. 1827)
S. Theodore Felstead, *Stars Who Made the Halls,* 1946.
Gracie Fields, *Sing As We Go,* 1960.
Frank Foster (with William G. Bosworth), *Clowning Through,* 1927.
Roland Gelatt, *The Fabulous Phonograph,* 1956.
Douglas Gilbert, *American Vaudeville,* 1940.
Maurice Gorham, *Showmen and Suckers,* n.d.
Grock, *Life's a Lark,* 1931.
    King of Clowns, 1957.
Corney Grain, *Corney Grain,* 1888.
George Grossmith, *A Society Clown,* 1888.
Stuart Hall and Paddy Whannel, *The Popular Arts,* 1964.
Thomas Hudson, *Comic Songs,* 9 volumes, 1818-1828.

Naomi Jacob, *Our Marie*, 1936.
Ted Kavanagh, *Tommy Handley*, 1949.
Dan Leno, *Hys Booke*, 1899 (actually by T. C. Elder).
W. Macqueen-Pope, *The Melodies Linger On*, 1950.
                    Ghosts and Greasepaint, 1951.
                    Marie Lloyd, Queen of the Music Halls, n.d.
Raymond Mander and Joe Mitchenson, *British Music Hall*, 1965.
Pierre Mariel, *Paris Revue*, 1962.
Edward B. Marks, *They All Had Glamour*, 1944
G. J. Mellor, *Pom-Poms and Ruffles*, 1966.
Billy Merson, *Fixing the Stoof Oop*, n.d.
W. H. Morton and H. Chance Newton, *Sixty Years of Stage Service*, 1905.
E. Nerman, *Darlings of the Gods*, n.d. (1929?)
H. Chance Newton, *Cues and Curtain Calls*, 1927.
                    'Idols' of the Halls, 1928.
Christopher Pulling, *They Were Singing*, 1952.
Harry Reynolds, *Minstrel Memories*, 1928.
Arthur Roberts, *Fifty Years of Spoof*, 1927.
George Robey, *Looking Back on Life*, 1933.
Clarkson Rose, *Beside the Seaside*, 1960.
                    Red Plush and Greasepaint, 1964.
George Rowell, *The Victorian Theatre*, 1952.
G. F. Scotson-Clark (and George Gamble), *The Halls*, c. 1898.
Harold Scott, *English Song Book*, 1925.
                    The Early Doors, 1946.
Stephen Sedley, *The Seeds of Love*, 1967.
Chris Shaw and Arthur Oates, *A Pictorial History of the Art of Female Impersonation*, 1966.
Leslie Shepard, *The Broadside Ballad*, 1962.
Ernest Short, *Fifty Years of Vaudeville*, 1946.
Ashley Sterne and Archibald de Bear, *The Comic History of the Co-optimists*, 1926.
W. M. Thackeray, *The History of Pendennis*, 1849-50.
                    The Newcomes, 1854-55.
Robert Tressell, *The Ragged Trousered Philanthropists*, 1955.
Stanley Wells, "Shakespearean Burlesque," *Shakespeare Quarterly*, 1965.
John Willett, *Brecht on Theatre*, 1964.
A. E. Wilson, *Prime Minister of Mirth*, 1956.
Francis Worsley, *ITMA*, 1948.

Recordings

It would, perhaps, be more frustrating than helpful to give here a complete list of the records consulted in the preparation of this book. I give below a selection of records which are either still in manufacturers' catalogues or have only recently gone out of production and might still be available. The list does not set out to be a complete discography but it does offer examples of re-recordings of discs made as long as sixty-five years ago as well as more recent revivals in different styles. All the records are twelve-inch l.p.s and all are mono unless stated to the contrary.

Top of the Bill, Fidelio, ATL 4010: re-recording of songs by Marie Lloyd (2), Harry Lauder (2), Albert Chevalier (2), Eugene Stratton (2), Florrie Forde (2), Dan Leno, Little Tich.

Golden Age of the Music Hall, Delta, TQD 3030: re-recordings of songs from records made prior to World War I by Dan Leno (2), Albert Chevalier (2), Marie Lloyd (2), Arthur Roberts, George Robey, Gus Elen, Vesta Victoria, Louis Bradfield, Henry Lytton, Little Tich, and Florrie Forde.

Laugh with the Old-Timers, Vocal Art, Recital 26. Privately issued disc by James Crawley re-recording cylinders made by Florrie Forde (4), Vess Osmann, W. H. Berry, Gus Elen, Vesta Tilley, Arthur Osmond, Billy Williams, Billy Murray, G. H. Chirgwin, Victoria Monks, and Billy Whitlock.

Gus Elen Sings; a first-rate re-recording of 14 of Elen's songs issued by the British Music Hall Society. It has the added merit of not including those songs available on Fidelio, Delta, and Decca recordings.

Golden Voices of Music Hall, Decca, ACL 1077; two songs each by Ella Shields, Tom Leamore, Nellie Wallace, Gus Elen, Hetty King, and Albert Whelan.

Gracie Fields; two selections available on Decca, ACL 1107 and ACL 1122.

George Formby Junior; two selections available on Decca, ACL 1062 and ACL 1145.

Max at the Met, Pye, GGL 0195; an excellent impression of Max Miller's act as given before a full house at the Metropolitan, Edgware Road, London, at the end of his (and the theatre's) career.

She Was Poor But She Was Honest, Folkways, FW 8707; first-rate programme of music-hall songs and melodrama by Derek Lamb. The presentation is intimate, making no attempt to recapture the 'original spirit' of the halls (as do the Late Joys), but instead has a contemporary audience in mind. The arrangements are made with discrimination and tact. A booklet with words is provided.

Late Joys, Decca, Stereo, SKL 4628 (but available on mono). A live performance of songs from the Players' Theatre, London, which attempts, with some success, to recapture the music-hall spirit when it was still customary to have a chairman (here Don Gemmel). There are nineteen songs, several excellent performances, and audience participation. The mood is a little forced and the performances sometimes slightly exaggerated.

...the 'ouses in between, Reality, RY 1004; fifteen cockney music-hall songs sung by John Foreman.

Cockney Music Hall Songs, Tradition, 1017; sung by Colyn Davies.

Tommy Armstrong of Tyneside, Topic, 12T122. Not really a music-hall disc but a fine collection of songs by the great ballad writer of North-East England. It includes "Wor Nanny's a Mazor" (also found, in another version on *Songs of the Tyne*, Delyse, ECB 3169).

General Index

(Illustrations are indicated by italicized page numbers.)

Abingdon, William, 79
Absurd humour, 11, 60, 113, 117, 151, 166
Afterword, 229-37
Albee, Edward, 61
Albion's Nationality, 67
Alhambra programme, 31
Alienation effect, 234-5
A Little Bit of Cucumber, 204-7
A Little of What You Fancy Does You Good, 105
A Motto for Every Man, 26-29
And Her Golden Hair Was Hanging Down Her Back, 84-84, 104
Andy Capp, 44
Any Old Iron, 206-7
Are We To Part Like This, Bill?, 80-82
'Arf a Pint of Ale, 198-200, 207
Armstrong, Tommy, 33, 41, 44
Army of Today's Alright, The, 138
Arthur, Jack, 219
Askey, Arthur, 227
A Thing He'd Never Done Before, 152-56, 160
At My Time of Life, 63-67
Audience attitudes and relationships, 15, 24-25, 60, 72-73, 79, 86, 100-1, 113, 160-1, 230, 231, 232, 235.

Bandwaggon, 151, 227
Bang Went the Chance of a Lifetime, 157-61
Banshee, The, 96
Bantock, Sir Granville, 160
Barclay's Beer, 19
Bard, Wilkie, 66-7
Barnes, F.J., 77
Bastow, George, 40
Bateman, Edgar, 192, 194
Beaumont and Fletcher, 52
Beckett, Samuel, 25, 29, 53, 215
Bedford, programme, *45*
Beerbohm, Max, 60, 71, 73, 76, 127
Bellwood, Bessie, *34,* 37, 38, 82, 160
Benny, J. 15
Bethell, S.L., 24, 232
Bibliography, 238-39
Bird in Nellie's Hat, The, 86
Blaydon Races, 33
Blind Boy, The, 122
Bloom, Sol, 160
Boiled Beef and Carrots, 206-7
Booth, J.B., 10, 117
Brecht, B., 234-5, *237*
Burlington Bertie from Bow, 139
By Jingo, 66

Calligan, Call Again, 172
Campbell, Herbert, *55,* 61, 63, 65-67, 166
Campbell, Marie, *222*

Canterbury Music Hall, 9, 14, *217, 218*
Caretaker, The, 53
Carney, Kate, *80,* 82
Carter, F.W., 124
Castling, Harry, 80, 167
Catcheside-Warrington, C.E., 30, 41, 44, 46
Champagne Charlie, 16-19, 33, 95, 139
Champion, Harry, 201, 203, 204, *206,* 207
Chant, Mrs. Ormiston, 86
Chester, Alf, 76
Chevalier, Albert, 25, 60, 82, 99, 105, 167, 182, *184,* 185-8, 190-1, 194
Chickaleary Cove, The, 185
Chirgwin, G.H., 53, 90, 118, *120,* 122-3, 203
Churchill, Sir Winston, 117
Clare, Emil, 162, 166-7
Clifton, Harry, 19, 26, *28,* 29-30, 33
Cliquot, 19
Clyde, van der 65, 138
Cockney Tragedian, The 167
Coffin, Hayden, 67
Collins, Charles, 80, 220
Connor, T.W., 63, 114, 204, 212
Conrad, Joseph, 187
Conroy, Peter, 88
Coote, Charles, 26, 28
Coster's Christening, The, 105
Cotes, C.G., 148
Coward, Noel, 187
Cowell, Sam, 20, 24, *25,* 166
Coyne, Frank, 124, 127
Critical Problems, 10-11, 52, 54, 122-23, 146-47, 229-37
Crook, John, 186, 188
Cunliffe, Whit, 165, 167
Cushie Butterfield, 30-33, 48-49, 76, 184, 186-87
Cyder Cellars, 14, 180

Daddy Wouldn't Buy me a Bow-wow, 40
Daly, Brian, 188
'Dame' tradition, 65, 138
Dance, George, 88, 91
Darewski, Herman, 166
Darnley, Herbert, 68
David, Worton, 162, 166-67
Dickens, Charles, 117
Dilke, Sir Charles, 236
Direct Address, 15, 232-35
Disher, M, Willson, 10, 52, 53, 113, 134, 166, 214
Dodd, Ken, 171-72
Do It No More, 66
Don't Go Out Tonight, Dear Father, 50-54
Drag, 65, 138-39
Dramatic Implications of Music Hall, 232-36
Dunville, T.E., 114, *116,* 117

Ealing Film Studios, 19
Earle, Fred, 40, 177
'E Can't Take a Roize Out of Oi, 190
Elder, T.C., 60
Elen, Gus, 25, 99, 105, 184, 186, 192, 194-96, *198*, 200, 223
Eliot, T.S., 15, 99
Elliott, Sumner Locke, 100
Entertainer, The, 53, 72, 160, 235
Eplett, F., 56
Evans's Supper Rooms, 14, 24
Everard, George, 144
Every Little Movement, 102-5

Fallen Star, The, 82, 185-86
Farren, Nelly, 34
Father, Dear Father, 53
Fields, Gracie, 53, 224, 227, *228*
Fire Was Burning Hot, The, 114-17
Following in Father's Footsteps, 136-39
Fol-the-rol-lol, 127
Forde, Florrie, 90, 165, 167
Forde, J., 237
Foreword, 8-11
Formby, Sr., George, 32, 40, 99, 105, 131, 212, *214*, 215-16, 218-19, 223
Formby Jr. George, 218-19
Fox, George, D., 132
Foy, Tom, *32*
Fragson, Harry, 162, 167
Frankau, Gilbert, 65
Fregoli, Leopoldo, 138
Frost, David, 130
Funny Phrases, 167
Future Mrs. 'Awkins, The, 76, 96, 182-87, 195
Fyffe, Will, *32*, 172

Galsworthy, John, 187
Gamble, George, 99
Gammond, Peter, 223
Gatti's Music Hall, *173*
George, Muriel and Ernest Butcher, 20
Gilbert, W.S., 90, 151, 215
Girdlestone, Madge, *222*
Goon Show, The, 113, 227
Gordon, Alf, 181

Half-Past Nine, 76, 220-23
Hall, Stuart, and Paddy Whannell, 8
Hancock, Tony, 155, 227
Handley, Tommy, 227
Hargreaves, William, 167
Haverbach, O. A., 102
Have You Paid the Rent?, 201-3
Heaven Will Protect an Honest Girl, 104, 224-228
Heffron, J.C., 208, 211

Herbert, Will, 34
He's Going to Marry Mary Ann, 38-40
Hicks, Sir Seymour, 62, 79, 84, 86
Hildebrandt Montrose, 65
Hill, Jenny, 67, 138, 222
His Lordship Winked at the Counsel, 88-91
Hobson, M., 26
Holborn Empire, 228
Holt, Fred, 200
Home, Sweet, Home, 134
Honeysuckle and the Bee, The, 79, 160
Hoschna, K., 102
Howerd, Frankie, 15, 61, 155
Hudd, Roy, 60
Hudson, Thomas, 180
Hunt, G.W., 66-67
Hunter, Harry, 118, 122, 166
Huntsman, The, 56-62
Hurley, Alec, 19, 91, 99, 186, 194, *197*

I Ain't a-going to Hell, 19
If it Wasn't for the Houses in Between, 82, 96,192-96
If You Were the Only Girl in the World, 155
I Live in Trafalgar Square, 128-31, 139
I'll Place it in the Hands of My Solicitor, 90
I May be Crazy, 96
I'm Henery the Eighth I Am, 207
I'm One of the Ruins that Cromwell Knocked Abaht a Bit, 109
Ingle, Charles, 185
In my 'Ansom, 86
Innuendo, 86, 104-5, 143, 151, 180, 215, 219
Irving, Henry, 24, 233
Ison, George, 34
Is Yer Mammie Always with Ye?, 95
Itma, 151, 227
It's a Different Girl Again, 165, 167
It's Alright in the Summertime, 144-47
I've Got Rings on my Fingers, 77-79
I've Never Lost my Last Train Yet, 104, 106-9

Jacques, Hattie, 143
Jeerussalem's Dead, 96, 139, 188-91
Jingoism, 66-67
Just Before the Battle Mother, 54

Keep Your Feet Still, Geordie Hinney, 46-49
Kendall, A.B., 168
King, Harry, 74
Kipling, Rudyard, 187

Lamb, Derek, 66
Lambeth Walk, The, 139, 186

Lamont, Alfred, 152
Lashwood, George, 127
Lauder, Harry, 32, *168, 171,* 172, 174, 176
Leamar, Alice, 84
Le Brunn, George, 106, 192, 195, 216, 223
Lee, Alfred, 16, 224
Leigh, Fred W., 140
Leno, Dan, 40, *56,* 60-62, *62,* 65, 68, 71, *72,* 73-74, *75,* 76, 166, 214, 234
Let's All Go Down the Strand, 164, 167
Levin, Bernard, 130
Leybourne, George, 16, *17, 18,* 19, 40, 105, 185
Lilly Dale, 52
Lily of Laguna, 92-97
Lion Comique, 19, 139, 200
Lipton, Dan, 167
Little Tich, 110, *112,* 113, 117
Lloyd, Arthur, 90
Lloyd, Marie, 37, 86, 91, 98-101, 102, *104,* 105, 106, 108-9, 215, 227
Lodge, David, 207
London, The, *126*
London Pavilion, *40,*228; programme, *131*
London Pride, 187
Look Back In Anger, 52, 95
Lord Lovell, 24

Macdermott, G.H., 65, 66
Macqueen-Pope, W., 10, 15, 19, 29, 95-97, 100, 122, 166, 172, 185, 194
Maeterlinck, M., 96
Maid's Tragedy, The, 52
Man was a Stranger to Me, The, 212-15
Marlowe, Christopher, 237
McGlennon, Felix, 84
Metropolitan, The, *133,* 227
Mill, Paul, 132, 134
Miller Max, 72-73, 86, 160, 227
Milligan, J.H., 174
Mills, A.J., 98, 124
Miner's Dream of Home, The, 134
Morton, Charles, 9, 14, 24, 90
Mosedale, Teddy, 186, 191
Mother's Advice, 86
Motto songs, 28-29
Mr. John Mackie, 172
Multiconsciousness (and examples), 24-25, 53, 67, 130, 134, 143, 176, 187, 190-1, 195, 228, 230, 232-34
Murphy, C.W., 128, 152, 167
Murray, Fred, 144
Music halls, development, 8-10
Music-Hall Shakespeare, The, 162-67
My Chestnut 'Orse, 186
My Fiddle is my Sweetheart, 118-123
My Fiddle was my Sweetheart, 120-23

My Old Dutch, 185, 186
My Old Man said Follow the Van, 105

Nanny, 174-76
Nellie Gray, 46
Newcomes, The, 9, 14
Newton, F. Chance, 10, 15, 37, 40, 53, 86, 90, 99-100, 119, 122-123, 138, 160, 166, 185-86, 195, 222
Night I Appeared as Macbeth, The, 167
Norrible Tale or The Suicidal Family, 24
Nosmo King, 116

O'Casey, Sean, 53, 156, 211
Oh, Oh, Antonio, 165, 167
One of the Deathless Army, 110-13
Osborne, Charles, 120
Osborne, John, 52-53, 72, 95, 160, 235
Othello, 49
Oxford, The, *48, 51*

Palace, programme, *30*
Parody, 66-67, 130, 166, 231
Pendennis, 14
Penny Whistler, 132-34
Pether, Henry, E., 140
Philaster, 52
Pike, Ernest, 54
Pink, Wal, 223
Pinter, Harold, 25, 53
Playing the Game in the West, 218
Please Sell No More Drink to my Father, 52
Pop Goes the Weasel, 24
Prehistoric Man, 148-51
Pretty Polly Perkins, 28, 33
Pulling, Christopher, 9, 10, 14, 24, 40, 65, 90, 139, 167, 180
Punning, 122-23, 203, 215, 236

Ragged Trousered Philanthropists, The, 28, 79
Ratcatcher's Daughter, The, 24
Recordings, 240
Reed, Leslie, 208
Richard II, 122-23
Rickards, Harry, 88, 90, *91*
Ridley, George, 30-31, 33
Roberts, Arthur, 90, 91
Robey, George, 67, 148, *150,* 151-152, *154,* 155-57, *159,* 160-61, 185, 233
Robson, Frederick, 20, 24-25, 53, 228, 230
Rogers, E.W., 136
Rohmer, Sax, 157, 160
Rollit, George, 106

Rose, Clarkson, 227
Ross, W. G., *12*, 13-15, 166
Royal Holborn, programme, *179*
Rusty Bugles, 100
Rule, Fred, 200

Salvation Army, 19, 127, 156
Sam Hall, 13-15, 97
Scott, Bennett, 98
Scott, Clement, 67, 86
Scott, Malcolm, 138
Seaweed, 177-81
Shakespeare, William, 49, 52, 122-23, 138, 155, 166-67 215,
    231, 237
Shall I be an Angel, Daddy?, 67
Shaw, G.B., 60, 90, 127, 187, 231
She Was Poor But She Was Honest, 104
Shields, Ella, 139
Silberman, L., 200
Simpson, H., 120
Since Poor Father Joined the Territorials, 113
Soldiers of the Queen, 67, 96
Spencer, T., 113
Stevens, G.A., 56
St. John, Florence, 37
Stoll, Sir Oswald, 227
Stratton, Eugene, 92, 95
Strindberg, J.A., 215
Stuart, Leslie, 67, 92, 95-97, 190
Sullivan, Sir Arthur, 90, 96
Sweetheart May, 96, 190
Swimming Master, The, 68-73

Tabrar, Joseph, 38, 40, 180
Taylor, Dan, 219
Temperance songs, 52-54
Tempest, Charles, 198
Temple Jr., R., 148
Terriss, Ellaline, 77, *78*, 79, 86
Terriss. William, 79
Terry, Will, 110
Textual Variations, 10, 14-15, 33, 43, 44-45, 73, 150-51, 161,
    181
Thackeray, W.M., 8-9, 14, 51
That's the Reason Noo I Wear a Kilt, 168-172, 200
There's a Wee Hoose on the Hillside, 176
Thompson, S.L., 50
Thurban, T.W., 110
Tichborne, Roger, 112
Tilley, Vesta, 96, 105, 136, 138-39, 190
Ting, Ting, that's how the Bell Goes, 19, 40
Tivoli, programme, *76, 83, 87*
Toole, J.L., 20, 24
Travers, Hyram, 186

Tresahar, Helen, 61-62
Tressell, Robert, 19, 28-29, 79, 227
Trewin, J.C., 231
Trial By Jury, 90
Trinder, Tommy, 19, 160, 219
Trollope, A., 52
Twiggy-Vous, 115

Vance, Alfred (The Great Vance), 19, 105, 185
Verdi, Ruby, *222*
Verfremdungseffekt, 234-35
Victoria, Vesta, 25, 40, 76, *135*, 140, *142*, 143, *146*, 147, 223
Villikins and his Dinah, 20-25, 228

Waiting at the Church, 76, 96, 139, 140-43, 146-47, 160, 184,
    223
Waiting for Godot, 53
Wallace, Nellie, 99, *220, 222*, 223
War Correspondent, The, 117
We All Go to Work but Father, 76, 156, 200, 208-11
We All Went Home in a Cab, 139, 186, 216-19
Weepin' Willer, 28, 143
Wells, Gilbert, 110
Wells, Stanley, 167
We Parted on the Shore, 176
West, Alfred, 186
Weston, R.P., 77, 224
What Did She Know About Railways?, 108
When I'm Cleaning Windows, 219
When I Take my Morning Promenade, 98-101, 104
Whittle, Charles, 164, 167
Williams, Billy, 214
Wilson, A.E., 155
Wilson, Joe, 33, 46, 48
Wincott, Harry, 216
Wood, Daisy (sister of Marie Lloyd), *109*
Work, Boys, Work and be Contented, 28-29
Wor Nanny's a Mazer, 41-45
Wotcher 'Ria, 34-38, 82
Would You be Surprised to Hear?, 90
Wright, Lawrence, 167

You'll Never be an Angel Daddy, 67, 130
Young Man Taken in and Done for, 71, 74-76
You've Got a Long Way to Go, 124-27, 134

Zoo Story, The, 61

(Passing references are, in the main, omitted.)